Holt McDougal Geometry

Geometry Lab Activities

HOLT McDOUGAL

HOUGHTON MIFFLIN HARCOURT

COMMON
CORE
EDITION

ISBN 978-0-547-71042-6

1 2 3 4 5 6 7 8 9 10   0928   20 19 18 17 16 15 14 13 12 11

4500303623   ^ B C D E F G

Contents

Holt McDougal Geometry

Contents continued

Holt McDougal Geometry

LESSON 1-2

Foundations for Geometry

Technology Lab Recording Sheet: Explore Properties Associated with Points

For use with the lesson Measuring and Constructing Segments

Try This

1. Repeat the activity with a new segment. Drag each of the points in your figure (the endpoints, the point on the segment, and the midpoint). Write down any relationships you observe about the measurements.

   - Construct a segment and label its endpoints A and C.

   - Create point B on $\overline{AC}$.

   - What is $\overline{AB}$? _____

   - What is $\overline{BC}$? _____

   - What is the sum of AB and BC? _____

   - What is the length of $\overline{AC}$? _____

   - What do you notice about the length of $\overline{AC}$ compared with the measurements of AB and BC? _____

   - Drag point B along $\overline{AC}$. Drag one of the endpoints of $\overline{AC}$. What relationship do you think are true about the three measurements?

     _____

     _____

   - Construct the midpoint of $\overline{AC}$ and label it M.

   - What is $\overline{AM}$? _____

   - What is $\overline{MC}$? _____

   - What relationships do you think are true about the lengths of $\overline{AC}$, $\overline{AM}$, and $\overline{MC}$? Use the Calculate tool to confirm your findings.

     _____

     _____

   - How many midpoints of $\overline{AC}$ exist? _____

> Draw a sample of your segment.

2. Create a point D not on $\overline{AC}$. Measure $\overline{AD}$, $\overline{DC}$, and $\overline{AC}$.

   AD = _____; DC = _____; AC = _____

   Does AD + DC = AC? _____
   What do you think has to be true about D for the relationship to always be true? _____

> Draw a sample of your segment.

Holt McDougal Geometry

LESSON
1-2

Foundations for Geometry

Geometry Lab: Measuring Lines Using Customary and Metric Rulers
Use with the lesson Measuring and Constructing Segments

Line segments can be measured because they have two endpoints. You can use
either a customary or metric ruler to measure a segment, depending on the units
required. The method to measure a segment is the same no matter which ruler is
used, however, the length of a segment is only as precise as the smallest unit on
the ruler.

Materials needed: Customary and Metric Ruler

Activity
Find the length of $\overline{AB}$, to the nearest eighth of an inch.

A   B
●————————————————————————————————●

(1) Place the 0-inch mark, or the left edge of a customary ruler at point *A*. Align the
ruler on the segment as shown.

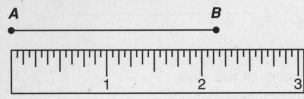

(2) Read the measure on the ruler at point *B*. Point *B* is slightly to the left
of the $\frac{3}{16}$-inch mark, so the segment is $2\frac{1}{8}$ inches long, to the nearest
eighth of an inch.

Try This
Measure each segment to the nearest eighth of an inch and to the nearest
half of a centimeter.

1.   2.

3.   4.

5.

6.

Holt McDougal Geometry

LESSON
1-2

Foundations for Geometry

**Geometry Lab: Measuring Lines Using Customary and
Metric Rulers** continued

7. _____ _____

8. **Critical Thinking** In Exercises 1–7, which two line segments are congruent?
   Explain.

   _____

Name _____ Date _____ Class _____

Foundations for Geometry

Geometry Lab: Index Card Protractor
Use with the lesson Measuring and Constructing Angles

When a protractor is not available you can quickly make an angle-measuring device out of an index card. You can use this home-made protractor to estimate angle measurements and to quickly classify an angle.

Materials needed: Index card, or similar

Activity

(1) On the index card, draw the rays forming the right angle at the bottom left corner.
  • A right angle has a measure of 90°.
  • Any angle greater than this measure is an obtuse angle.
  • Any angle smaller than this angle is an acute angle.

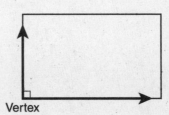
Vertex

(2) Fold the top left corner of the index card down so that it meets the bottom edge of the card. Press on the fold so that it creases the card. This crease indicates a 45° angle.

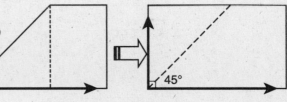

(3) Now fold the top left corner of the index card down so that it meets the crease of the 45° mark. Press on the fold so that it creases the card. This crease indicates a 60° angle.

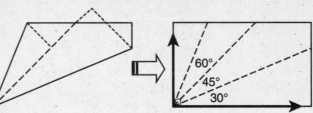

(4) Then fold the bottom left corner up so that it meets the crease of the 45° mark. Press on the fold so that it creases the card. This crease indicates a 30° angle.

Try This

Use your index-card protractor to classify each angle as right, obtuse, or acute and then estimate the approximate measure of each angle.

1.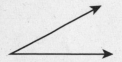

2.

3.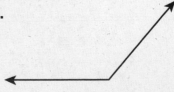

_____   _____   _____

Holt McDougal Geometry

Foundations for Geometry

LESSON 1-3

Geometry Lab: Index Card Protractor continued

4.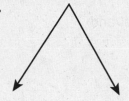

_____

5.

_____

6.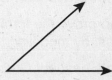

_____

Name _____ Date _____ Class _____

Foundations for Geometry

LESSON
1-5A

Geometry Lab A: Using Models to Justify Area and Perimeter Formulas
Use with the lesson Using Formulas in Geometry

You can prove the formulas for area and perimeter of rectangles, squares, and triangles, by modeling the figures on a grid paper.

Materials needed: Grid paper

Activity 1
Perimeter of a Rectangle

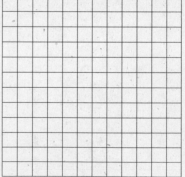

(1) Draw and label rectangle *ABCD* on grid paper.

(2) By counting the squares find the length of each side length:
AB = _____   CD = _____
BC = _____   DA = _____

(3) The perimeter of a rectangle is the sum of the lengths of the sides. Using the lengths in Step 2, find the perimeter of *ABCD*. _____

(4) Let *AB* equal the length, ℓ. So $\ell = 10$.
Let *BC* equal the width, *w*. So *w* = 4.
The formula for perimeter of a rectangle is $P = 2\ell + 2w$.
Substitute the known values into the formula and solve for *P*.
$P = 2\ell + 2w = 2(10) + 2(4) = $ _____

(5) In Step 3 you calculate the perimeter of *ABCD* by finding the sum of each side length and in Step 4 you calculated the perimeter by using the formula. Did both methods in the same answer? _____ Did you justify the formula? _____

Try This

1. Justify the formula for the area of rectangle *ABCD*.

_____

_____

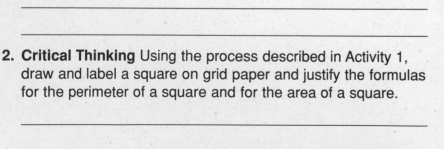

2. **Critical Thinking** Using the process described in Activity 1, draw and label a square on grid paper and justify the formulas for the perimeter of a square and for the area of a square.

_____

_____

3. **Make a Conjecture** Use rectangle *ABCD* in Activity 1 to justify the area of the triangle formula for triangle *ADC*.

_____

_____

Holt McDougal Geometry

Name _____ Date _____ Class _____

Foundations for Geometry

Geometry Lab B: Area of a Rectangle
Use with the lesson Using Formulas in Geometry

It is possible for two or more rectangles to have the same area, but different perimeters. Why is this? It is because the measure of the length and width differs.

Materials needed: Grid paper and scissors

Activity
Determine the possible dimensions of a rectangle given that the area of the rectangle measures 32 square units.

(1) Using grid paper, cut out various rectangles that have an area of 32 square units. Use only whole number side lengths.

List the length and width of each rectangle that you cut out.

_____

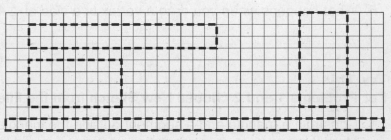

(2) The factors of 32 are listed below. These factors are all possible side lengths of rectangles with an area of 32 square units. If you did not cut out all of the possible rectangles, do so now.

1 × 32; 2 × 16; 4 × 8; 8 × 4; 16 × 2; 32 × 1

(3) Find the perimeter for each rectangle that you cut out.

_____

(4) Which rectangle has the greatest area? _____

(5) Which rectangle has the smallest perimeter? _____

Try This
Use grid paper to cut out all possible dimensions of a rectangle with the given area. List the possible dimensions.

1. A rectangle with an area of 16 square units _____

2. A rectangle with an area of 25 square units _____

3. A rectangle with an area of 36 square units _____

4. **Critical Thinking** The dimensions of a rectangle with an area of 16, 25, 36, or any other perfect square, always result in the smallest perimeter when the length is _____ to the width.

7

Holt McDougal Geometry

Foundations for Geometry

LESSON 1-7

Technology Lab Recording Sheet: Explore Transformations with Geometry Software

For use with the lesson Transformations in the Coordinate Plane

Try This

Activity 1

4. What do you notice about the relationship between your preimage and its image?

_____

5. What happens when you drag a vertex or a side of △ABC?

_____

Try This

For Problems 1 and 2 choose New Sketch from the File menu.

1. Construct a triangle and a segment outside the triangle. Mark this segment as a translation vector as you did in Step 2 of Activity 1. Use Step 4 of Activity 1 to translate the triangle. What happens when you drag an endpoint of the new segment?

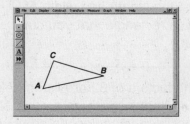

_____

2. Instead of translating by a marked vector, use RECTANGULAR as the translation vector and translate by a horizontal distance of 1 cm and a vertical distance of 2 cm. Compare this method with the marked vector method. What happens when you drag a side or vertex of the triangle?

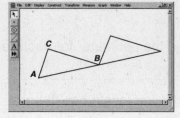

_____

3. Sketch the angles and sides of the preimage and image triangle. Use the tools in the Measure menu to measure length, angle measure, and area. What do you think is true about these two figures?

_____

_____

_____

Holt McDougal Geometry

Name _____ Date _____ Class _____

Geometric Reasoning
Geometry Lab Recording Sheet: Solve Logic Puzzles
Use with the lesson *Using Deductive Reasoning to Verify Conjectures*

Try This

Activity 1
Try This

1. After figuring out that Fiona owns the bird in Step 3, why can you place an X in every other box in that row and column?

   _____

2. Ally, Emily, Misha, and Tracy go to a dance with Danny, Frank, Jude, and Kian Ally and Frank are siblings. Jude and Kian are roommates. Misha does not know Kian. Emily goes with Kian's roommate. Tracy goes with Ally's brother. Who went to the dance with whom?

   _____

3. What combinations are unworkable?

   _____

   Why?

   _____

Activity 2
Try This

4. How many solutions are there to the farmer's transport problem?

   _____

   How many steps does each solution take?

   _____

Holt McDougal Geometry

LESSON 2-3

Geometric Reasoning

Geometry Lab Recording Sheet: Solve Logic Puzzles continued

5. What is the advantage of drawing a complete solution network rather than working out one solution with a diagram?

_____

_____

6. Madeline has two measuring cups—a 1-cup measuring cup and a $\frac{3}{4}$-cup measuring cup. Neither cup has any markings on it. How can Madeline get exactly $\frac{1}{2}$ cup of flour in the larger measuring cup? Complete the network below to solve the problem.

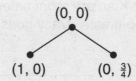

$(0, 0)$

$(1, 0)$ $(0, \frac{3}{4})$

Holt McDougal Geometry

Geometric Reasoning

Geometry Lab: Creating Booklets of BiConditional Statements

Use with the lesson Biconditional Statements and Definitions

Use everyday words and their definitions to create biconditional statements and determine whether the conditional and converse statements for the biconditional are true.

Materials needed: 3 sheets of blank white paper (8.5 × 11), dictionary

Activity

1. Fold Paper

   a. Fold sheet of paper in half.

   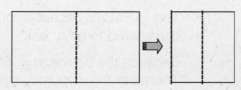

   b. Fold sheet of paper in half again.

   c. Unfold completely.

   d. Now fold outside flaps back in so it opens like a menu.

2. Look up the words "ball" and "cage" in the dictionary. Write their definitions and their biconditional statements on the front flaps of your booklet.

   Ex: **Definition:** Ball – any round or roundish body
   Biconditional: an object is a ball if and only if it has a round or roundish body

   Ex: **Definition:** Cage – an enclosure made of wires or bars
   Biconditional: an object is a cage if and only if it is made of wires or bars

Holt McDougal Geometry

LESSON 2-4

Geometric Reasoning

Geometry Lab: Creating Booklets of BiConditional Statements continued

3. Write the conditional and converse statements for each biconditional on the inside of your booklet. State whether each new statement is True or False.

   a. Conditional: Ball: If an object is a ball, then it has a round or roundish body. TRUE

   b. Converse: Ball: If an object has a round or roundish body, then it is a ball. FALSE

      • This is FALSE because not all "roundish" objects are considered to be a "ball"

      • Because the converse is FALSE, the biconditional is false. Therefore the dictionary definition is not a "good" definition.

   c. Conditional: Cage: If an object is a cage, then it is made of wires or bars. TRUE

   d. Converse: Cage: If an object is made of wires and bars, then it is a cage. FALSE

      • This is FALSE because not all objects made or wires or bars are considered to be a "cage"

      • Because the converse is FALSE, the biconditional is false. Therefore the dictionary definition is not a "good" definition.

Try This

Follow the process described above to create a booklet for the following words. Include the following:

   a. Write the definition of each word on the front of your booklet.

   b. Write the biconditional for each definition on the front of your booklet.

   c. State the conditional and converse statements for each biconditional on the inside of your booklet and whether or not it is True or False.

   d. If False, explain why.

1. Square, Hexagon

2. Queen, King

Holt McDougal Geometry

Name _____ Date _____ Class _____

Geometric Reasoning

LESSON 2-6

Geometry Lab Recording Sheet: Design Plans for Proofs

Use with the lesson Geometric Proof

Try This

Activity

6. Use the pieces in Steps 1–5 to write a complete two-column proof of the Common Angles Theorem.

Try This

1. Describe how a plan for a proof differs from the actual proof.

_____

_____

_____

_____

_____

_____

_____

Holt McDougal Geometry

LESSON 2-6 Geometric Reasoning

Geometry Lab Recording Sheet: Design Plans for Proofs continued

2. Write a plan and a two-column proof.

   Given: $\overrightarrow{BD}$ bisects $\angle ABC$.

   Prove: $2m\angle 1 = m\angle ABC$

3. Write a plan and a two-column proof.

   Given: $\angle LXN$ is a right angle.

   Prove: $\angle 1$ and $\angle 2$ are complementary.

Holt McDougal Geometry

Name _____ Date _____ Class _____

Geometric Reasoning
Technology Lab

Use with the lesson Flowchart and Paragraph Proofs

You can use The Geometer's Sketchpad to investigate the measures of angles of intersecting lines.

Activity

Step 1 Draw Intersecting Lines.

- Open a **New Sketch** under the **File** menu. Under the **Edit** menu, go to **Preferences** and set the labels to show automatically.

- Place one point *A* on the screen.

- Construct segment *BC* through point *A*.

- Construct another segment that intersects point *A* and $\overline{BC}$.

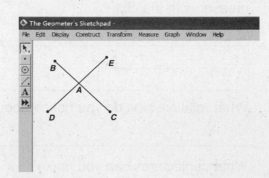

Step 2 Measuring Angles.

- Measure angle *BAD* by clicking on each point, in order of point *B*, point *A* and point *D*.

- Under the **Measure** menu, go to **Angles**. The measurement of ∠*BAD* will appear on screen. m∠BAD = 67.02°.

- Repeat this process to measure angle *EAC*.

    m∠*EAC* = _____

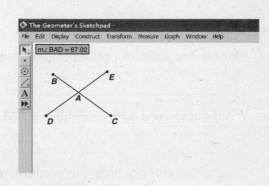

Try This

Answer each question.

1. Use The Geometer's Sketchpad for the following.

    a. Repeat Step 1 and Step 2 above for two more intersecting lines.

    b. Find the angle measures of all four angles:

    m∠*BAD* − _____; m∠*BAE* = _____; m∠*EAC* = _____; m∠*DAC* = _____

    c. What do you notice about the measures of the vertical angles?

    _____

2. How can you use your sketch in Exercise 1 to prove that the angle measures of adjacent angles are supplementary?

    _____

15   **Holt McDougal Geometry**

LESSON 3-2 **Parallel and Perpendicular Lines**
Technology Lab Recording Sheet: Explore Parallel Lines and Transversals

Use with the lesson Angles Formed by Parallel Lines and Transversals

Activity

4. Measure the angles formed by the parallel lines and the transversal. Write the angle measures in the chart below. Drag point *E* or *F* and fill in the new angle measures in the chart.

∠AGE	∠BGE	∠AGH	∠BGH	∠CHG	∠DHG	∠CHF	∠DHF

What relationships do you notice about the angle measures?

_____

What conjectures can you make?

_____

Try This

1. Identify the pairs of corresponding angles in the diagram.

_____

What conjecture can you make about their angle measures?

_____

Drag a point in the figure to confirm your conjecture. Can you confirm

your conjecture? _____

2. Repeat steps in the previous problem.

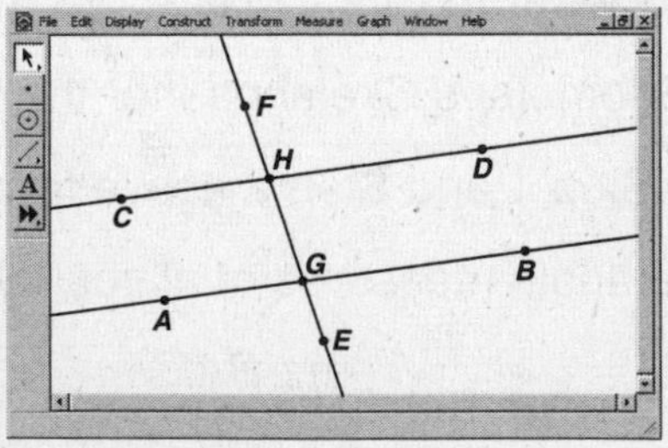

Identify the pairs of **alternate interior angles** in the diagram.

_____

What conjecture can you make about their angle measures?

_____

Holt McDougal Geometry

Parallel and Perpendicular Lines

Technology Lab Recording Sheet: Explore Parallel Lines and Transversals continued

Drag a point in the figure to confirm your conjecture. Can you confirm

your conjecture? _____

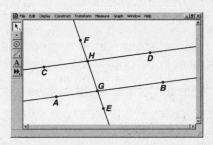

Identify the pairs of **alternate exterior angles** in the diagram.

_____

What conjecture can you make about their angle measures?

_____

Drag a point in the figure to confirm your conjecture. Can you confirm

your conjecture? _____

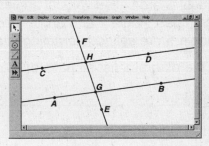

Identify the pairs of **same-side interior angles** in the diagram.

_____

What conjecture can you make about their angle measures?

_____

Drag a point in the figure to confirm your conjecture. Can you confirm

your conjecture? _____

3. Try dragging point C to change the distance between the parallel lines.

   What happens to the angle measures in the figure?

_____

What do you think this happens? _____

Holt McDougal Geometry

Name _____ Date _____ Class _____

Parallel and Perpendicular Lines
Geometry Lab: Investigating Angles Formed by Parallel Lines Cut by a Transversal

Use with the lesson Angles Formed by Parallel Lines and Transversals
Materials: protractor, paper and pencil

Activity

You and your partner are going to explore the relationship among the angles formed by a pair of parallel lines cut by a transversal.

Step 1 Measure each of the eight angles with a protractor and record your results.

m∠1 _____	m∠2 _____
m∠3 _____	m∠4 _____
m∠5 _____	m∠6 _____
m∠6 _____	m∠8 _____

Step 2 List all the pairs of congruent angles (12 pairs total).

_____

Angle 1 and angle 3 are called vertical angles. Angle 1 and Angle 5 are called corresponding angles. Angle 1 and angle 8 are called alternating exterior angles. Angle 3 and angle 5 are called alternating interior angles.

Step 3 Using the diagram, list all pairs of:

a. Vertical angles _____

b. Corresponding angles _____

c. Alternating Exterior angles _____

d. Alternating Interior angles _____

Try This
Using the table from Step 1, what conclusion can you draw about:

1. Vertical angles _____

2. Corresponding angles _____

3. Alternating Exterior angles _____

4. Alternating Interior angles _____

Holt McDougal Geometry

Parallel and Perpendicular Lines

LESSON 3-3 *Geometry Lab Recording Sheet: Construct Parallel Lines*

Use with the lesson Proving Lines Parallel

Try This

Activity 1
Try This

1. Repeat activity 1 using a different point not on the line.

You need a piece of paper.

Are your results the same?

_____

2. Using the lines you constructed in Problem 1, draw transversal $\overleftrightarrow{PQ}$. Verify that the lines are parallel by using a protractor to measure alternate interior angles.

3. What postulates ensures that this is always possible?

_____

4. A *rhombus* is a quadrilateral with four congruent sides. Explain why this method is called the rhombus method?

_____

_____

_____

_____

_____

_____

Holt McDougal Geometry

Name _____ Date _____ Class _____

Parallel and Perpendicular Lines
Geometry Lab Recording Sheet: Construct
Parallel Lines continued

Activity 2
Try This

5. Repeat Activity 2 using points in a different place not on the line.

You need a piece of paper.

Are your results the same?

_____

6. Use a protractor to measure corresponding angles. How can you tell that the lines are parallel?

_____
_____
_____
_____
_____

7. Draw a triangle and construct a line parallel to the one side through the vertex that is not on that side.

_____

8. Line *m* is perpendicular to both ℓ and *n*. use this statement to complete the following conjecture: If two lines in a plane are perpendicular to the same line,

then _____

20

Parallel and Perpendicular Lines

LESSON 3-4 *Geometry Lab Recording Sheet: Construct Perpendicular Lines*

Use with the lesson Perpendicular Lines

Try This

Copy each diagram and construct a line perpendicular to line ℓ, through point *P*. Use a protractor to verify that the lines are perpendicular.

1. Are the lines perpendicular? _____

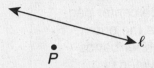

2. Are the lines perpendicular? _____

3. Following the steps below to construct two parallel lines. Explain why ℓ ∥ *n*.

Step 1	**Step 2**	**Step3**
Given a line ℓ, draw a point *P* not on ℓ.	Construct line *m* perpendicular to ℓ through *P*.	Construct line *n* perpendicular to *m* through *P*.

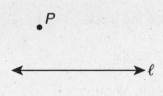 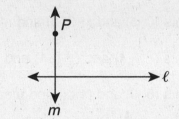 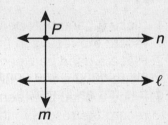

Holt McDougal Geometry

Name _____ Date _____ Class _____

LESSON
3-4
Parallel and Perpendicular Lines
Geometry Lab: Angles Formed by Perpendicular Lines

Use with the lesson Perpendicular Lines
Materials: Geoboard, bands (at least six) and pencil

You can apply what you have learned about perpendicular lines onto a Geoboard to investigate their slopes

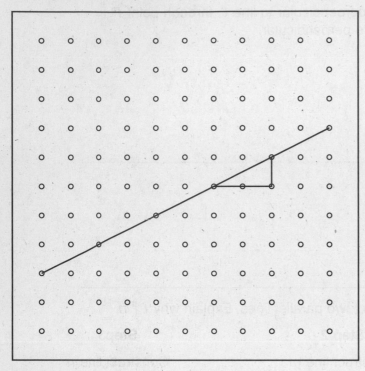

Some geoboards have a set of axes pre-drawn on them. If your geoboard does not, then locate the center peg, and mark it as the origin (0, 0). Use rubber bands stretched between two pegs to represent lines. For example, place one end of the band on the point (4, 2) and the other end on (−5, −3). You can calculate the slope of this line by drawing a right triangle anywhere on the line. The horizontal leg is 2 and the vertical leg is 1. The line climbs left to right, so the slope is $+\frac{1}{2}$.

Activity

Line 1 Place a band between the points (0, 5) and (−5, 0) and measure the slope, record the results in the table.

Line 2 Place a band between the points (−4, 4) and (−1, 1) and measure the slope, record the results in the table.

Line 3 Place a band between the points (5, 3) and (1, 2) and measure the slope, record the results in the table.

Line 4 Place a band between the points (2, 5) and (3, 1) and measure the slope, record the results in the table.

Line 5 Place a band between the points (−1, −1) and (−4, −3) and measure the slope, record the results in the table.

Line 6 Place a band between the points (−3, −1) and (−1, −4) and measure the slope, record the results in the table.

Line 7 Place a band between the points (5, −2) and (1,−2) and measure the slope, record the results in the table.

Holt McDougal Geometry

LESSON 3-4 Parallel and Perpendicular Lines
Geometry Lab: Angles Formed by Perpendicular Lines continued

Line 8 Place a band between the points (3, 0) and (3, −5) and measure the slope, record the results in the table.

Line	1	2	3	4	5	6	7	8
Slope								

Try This

1. Multiply the slope of line 1 times the slope of line 2. What is the product? _____

2. Multiply the slope of line 3 times the slope of line 4. What is the product? _____

3. Multiply the slope of line 5 times the slope of line 6. What is the product? _____

4. Characterize the relationship between the numerical slopes of the lines in each pair. _____

5. Characterize the relationship between the physical slopes (as on the geoboard) of the lines in each pair. _____

6. If you had two perpendicular lines and one had a slope of $\frac{3}{8}$, what is the slope of the other line? _____

7. In conclusion, two lines are perpendicular to each other if on a graph they intersect to form a _____ and their numerical slopes are _____.

8. **Critical Thinking** If you try to multiply the slope of line 7 times the slope of line 8, you hit a mathematical indeterminate situation. (You are multiplying 0 by infinity, which cannot be done.) Explain in your own words why these lines are perpendicular.

_____
_____
_____

Holt McDougal Geometry

Parallel and Perpendicular Lines

LESSON 3-5

Geometry Lab: Investigating Lines in the Coordinate Plane

Use with the lesson *Slopes of Lines*

Materials: Geoboard, bands (at least six) and pencil

You can apply what you have learned about linear equations onto a
Geoboard to investigate, describe and predict how changes to the slope
and *y*-intercept effect the line.

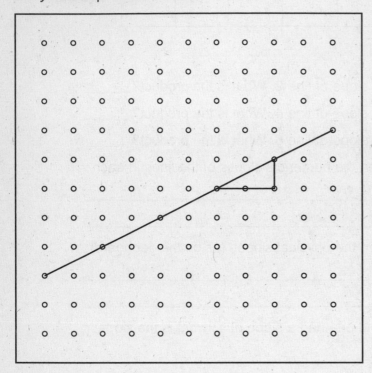

Some geoboards have a set
of axes pre-drawn on them.
If your geoboard does not,
then locate the center peg,
and mark it as the origin
(0, 0). Use rubber bands
stretched between two
pegs to represent lines.
For example, place one end
of the band on the point
(4, 2) and the other end on
(−5, −3). You can calculate
the slope of this line by
drawing a right triangle
anywhere on the line. The
horizontal leg is 2 and the
vertical leg is 1, and the line
climbs left to right, so the
slope is $+\frac{1}{2}$. You can also
determine the *y*-intercept,
which in this example is $-\frac{1}{2}$.

Activity 1

Line 1 Place a band between the points (2, 5) and (−4, 2) and measure the slope
and *y*-intercept, record the results in the table.

Line 2 Place a band between the points (5, 5) and (−3, 1) and measure the slope
and *y*-intercept, record the results in the table.

Line 3 Place a band between the points (2, 1) and (−4, −2) and measure the slope
and *y*-intercept, record the results in the table.

Line 4 Place a band between the points (4, −2) and (−2, −5) and measure the
slope and *y*-intercept, record the results in the table.

For the Position of Line, use descriptions with respect to the origin like: far above,
above, above & near, below & near, below, far below.

For Steepness use descriptions like: steep, moderate, gentle and for direction use
rising up or falling down (from left to right).

Holt McDougal Geometry

Name _____ Date _____ Class _____

Parallel and Perpendicular Lines

LESSON 3-5

Geometry Lab: Investigating Lines in the Coordinate Plane continued

Line	1	2	3	4
Numerical Slope				
y-intercept				
Position of Line				
Steepness/ Direction				

1. How would you characterize the relationship between the y-intercept and the

position of the line? _____

2. What would be the position of a line with y-intercept 75? _____

Activity 2

Line 1 Place a band between the points (1, 5) and (−3, −5) and measure the slope and y-intercept, record the results in the table.

Line 2 Place a band between the points (5, 5) and (−3, 1) and measure the slope and y-intercept, record the results in the table.

Line 3 Place a band between the points (5, 3) and (−5, 2) and measure the slope and y-intercept, record the results in the table.

Line 4 Place a band between the points (−3, 4) and (1, −4) and measure the slope and y-intercept, record the results in the table.

Line 5 Place a band between the points (−4, 1) and (4, −5) and measure the slope and y-intercept, record the results in the table.

Line 6 Place a band between the points (−4, −1) and (4, −3) and measure the slope and y-intercept, record the results in the table.

Line	1	2	3	4	5	6
Numerical Slope						
y-intercept						
Position of Line						
Steepness/ Direction						

3. How are the slope and the steepness of the line related? _____

4. What would be the steepness of a line with slope −50? _____

5. In conclusion, the slope determines the _____ and _____

of the line and the y-intercept determines the _____ of the line.

Holt McDougal Geometry

LESSON 3-6A

Parallel and Perpendicular Lines

Technology Lab Recording Sheet: Explore Parallel and Perpendicular Lines

Use with the lesson Lines in the Coordinate Plane

Try This

Activity 1

1. On a graphing calculator, graph the lines, $y = -3x - 4$ and on a standard window. Which lines appear to be parallel?

   _____

   What do you notice about the slopes of the parallel lines?

   _____

2. Graph $y = 2x$ on a square window. Experiment with other equations to find a line that appears parallel to $y = 2x$. If necessary, graph $y = 2x$ on graph paper

   and construct a parallel line. _____

   What is the slope of this new line? _____

3. Graph $y = -\frac{1}{2}x + 3$ on a square window. Try to graph a line that appears

   parallel to $y = -\frac{1}{2}x + 3$. _____

   What is the slope of this new line? _____

Try This

1. Create two new equations of lines that you think will be parallel. Graph these to confirm your conjecture.

   _____

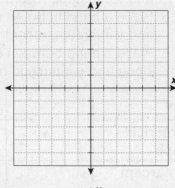

2. Graph two lines that you think are parallel.

   Change the window settings on the calculator. Do the

   lines still appear parallel? _____

   Describe your results.

   _____

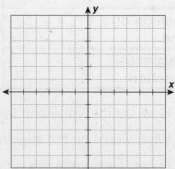

3. Try changing the *y*-intercepts of one of the parallel lines. Does this change whether the lines appear to be parallel?

   _____

Holt McDougal Geometry

Parallel and Perpendicular Lines

LESSON 3-6A

Technology Lab Recording Sheet: Explore Parallel and Perpendicular Lines continued

Activity 2

1. Graph the lines $y = x$ and $y = -x$ on a square window. Do the lines appear to be perpendicular? _____

2. Graph $y = 3x - 2$ on a square window. Experiment with other equations to find a line that appears perpendicular to $y = 3x - 2$. If necessary, graph $y = 3x - 2$ on graph paper and construct a perpendicular line. _____

   What is the slope of this new line? _____

3. Graph $y = \frac{2}{3}x$ on a square window. Try to graph a line that appears perpendicular to $y = \frac{2}{3}x$. _____

   What is the slope of this new line? _____

Try This

4. Create two new equations of lines that you think will be perpendicular.

   _____

   Graph these in a square window to confirm your conjecture.

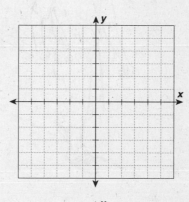

5. Graph two lines that you think are perpendicular.

   Change the window settings on the calculator. Do the lines still appear perpendicular?

   _____

   Describe your results.

   _____

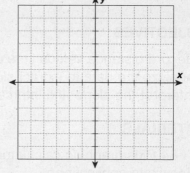

6. Try changing the y-intercepts of one of the perpendicular lines. Does this change whether the lines appear to be perpendicular?

   _____

Holt McDougal Geometry

Name _____ Date _____ Class _____

Parallel and Perpendicular Lines

Technology Lab

Use with the lesson *Lines in the Coordinate Plane*

When one quantity changes at a constant rate with respect to another, they are *linearly related*. Mathematically, this relationship is defined as a linear equation. In real-world applications, some quantities are linearly related and can be represented by using a straight-line graph.

In this activity, you will create straight-line, or constant-speed, distance versus time plots using a Motion Detector, and then develop linear equations to describe these plots mathematically.

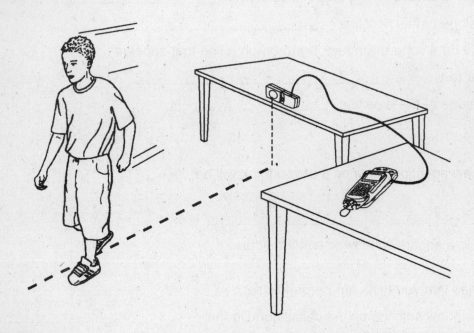

OBJECTIVES

• Record distance versus time data for a person walking at a uniform rate.
• Analyze the data to extract slope and intercept information.
• Interpret the slope and intercept information for physical meaning.

MATERIALS

TI-84 Plus graphing calculator
EasyData application
CBR 2 or Go! Motion and direct calculator cable
    or Motion Detector and data-collection interface

Parallel and Perpendicular Lines

LESSON 3-6B *Technology Lab* continued

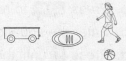

Activity 1

1. Set up the Motion Detector and calculator.

   a. Open the pivoting head of the Motion Detector. If your Motion Detector has a sensitivity switch, set it to Normal as shown.

   b. Turn on the calculator and make sure it is on the home screen. Connect it to the Motion Detector. (This may require the use of a data-collection interface.)

2. Position the Motion Detector on a table or chair so that the head is pointing horizontally out into an open area where you can walk. There should be no chairs or tables nearby.

3. Set up EasyData for data collection.

   a. Start the EasyData application, if it is not already running.

   b. Select ⌐File⌐ from the Main screen, and then select **New** to reset the application.

4. Stand about a meter from the Motion Detector. When you are ready to collect data, select ⌐Start⌐ from the Main screen. Walk away from the Motion Detector at a slow and steady pace. You will have five seconds to collect data.

5. When data collection is complete, a graph of distance versus time will be displayed. Examine the graph. It should show a nearly linearly increasing function with no spikes or flat regions. If you need to repeat data collection, select ⌐Main⌐ and repeat Step 4.

6. Once you are satisfied with the graph, select ⌐Main⌐ to return to the Main screen. Exit EasyData by selecting ⌐Quit⌐ from the Main screen and then selecting ⌐OK⌐.

ANALYSIS

1. Redisplay the graph outside of EasyData.

   a. Press `2nd` [STAT PLOT].

   b. Press `ENTER` to select Plot1 and press `ENTER` again to select On.

   c. Press `ZOOM`.

   d. Press ⬇ until ZoomStat is highlighted; press `ENTER` to display a graph with the *x* and *y* ranges set to fill the screen with data.

   e. Press `TRACE` to determine the coordinates of a point on the graph using the cursor keys.

2. The slope-intercept form of a linear equation is $y = mx + b$, where *m* is the slope of the line and *b* is the *y*-intercept value. The independent variable is *x*, which represents time, and *y* is the dependent variable, which represents distance in this activity. Trace across the graph to the left edge to read the *y*-intercept. Record this value as *b* in the Data Table.

3. One way to determine the slope of the distance versus time graph is to guess a value and then check it by viewing a graph of the line with your data. To do this, enter an equation into the calculator, and then enter a value for the *y*-intercept and store it as variable B.

Holt McDougal Geometry

Parallel and Perpendicular Lines

LESSON 3-6B *Technology Lab* continued

   a. Press `Y=` .

   b. Press `CLEAR` to remove any existing equation.

   c. Enter the equation M * X + B in the Y1 field.

   d. Press ◀ until the icon to the left of Y1 is blinking. Press `ENTER` until a bold diagonal line is shown in order to display your model with a thick line.

   e. Press `2nd` [QUIT] to return to the home screen.

   f. Enter your value for the *y*-intercept and then press `STO▶` B `ENTER` to store the value in the variable B.

4. Now set a value for the slope *m*, and then look at the resulting graph. To obtain a good fit, you will need to try several values for the slope. Use the steps below to store different values to the variable M. Start with M = 1. Experiment until you find one that provides a good fit.

   a. Enter a value for the slope *m* and press `STO▶` M `ENTER` to store the value in the variable M.

   b. Press `GRAPH` to see the data with the model graph superimposed.

   c. Press `2nd` [QUIT] to return to the home screen.

5. Record the optimized value for the slope in the Data Table. Use the values of the slope and intercept to write the equation of the line that best fits the distance versus time data.

6. Another way to determine the slope of a line to fit your data is to use two well-separated data points. Use the cursor keys to move along the data points. Choose two points (x_1, y_1) and (x_2, y_2) that are not close to each other and record them in the Data Table.

7. Use the points in the table to compute the slope, *m*, of the distance versus time graph.

$$\text{Use } m = \frac{y_2 - y_1}{x_2 - x_1}$$

to calculate the slope and answer Question 1 in the Try This section.

8. You can also use the calculator to automatically determine an optimized slope and intercept.

   a. Press `STAT` and use the cursor keys to highlight CALC.

   b. Press the number adjacent to LinReg(ax+b) to copy the command to the home screen.

   c. Press `2nd` [L1] `,` `2nd` [L6] `,` to enter the lists containing your data.

   d. Press `VARS` and use the cursor keys to highlight Y-VARS.

   e. Select Function by pressing `ENTER`.

   f. Press `ENTER` to copy Y1 to the expression.

   On the home screen, you will now see the entry LinReg(ax+b) L1, L6, Y1. This command will perform a linear regression using the *x*-values in L1 as and the *y*-values in L6. The resulting regression line will be stored in equation variable Y1.

   g. Press `ENTER` to perform the linear regression. Use the parameters a and b to write the equation of the calculator's best-fit line, and record it in the Data Table.

   h. Press `GRAPH` to see the graph.

Holt McDougal Geometry

Parallel and Perpendicular Lines
Technology Lab continued

DATA TABLE

y-intercept *b*	
optimized slope *m*	
optimized line equation	
x_1, y_1	
x_2, y_2	
regression line equation	

Try This

1. How does this value compare with the slope you found by trial and error?

   _____

   _____

2. How do the values of the slope and intercept as determined by the calculator compare to your earlier values? Would you expect them to be exactly the same?

   _____

   _____

   _____

   _____

3. Slope is defined as change in *y*-values divided by change in *x*-values. Complete the following statement about slope for the linear data set you collected.

   In this activity, slope represents a change in _____ divided by a change

   in _____ .

4. Based on this statement, what are the units of measurement for slope in this activity?

   _____

5. The *y*-intercept can be interpreted as the starting position or the starting distance from the Motion Detector. What does the slope represent physically?
   Hint: Consider the units of measurement for the slope you described in the previous question.

   _____

Holt McDougal Geometry

Name _____ Date _____ Class _____

LESSON 3-6C Parallel and Perpendicular Lines
Technology Lab

Use with page 199

Graphs made using a Motion Detector can be used to study motion. In this
experiment, you will use a Motion Detector to make graphs of your own motion.

OBJECTIVES

In this experiment, you will use a Motion Detector to measure distance and velocity;
produce graphs of your motion; analyze the graphs you produce.

MATERIALS

TI-84 Plus graphing calculator; EasyData application
CBR 2 Motion and direct calculator cable
 or Motion Detector and data-collection interface
masking tape; meter stick

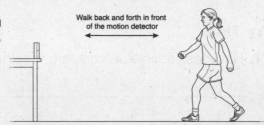

Walk back and forth in front
of the motion detector

Activity 1 Distance *vs.* Time Graphs

1. Fasten a Motion Detector to a tabletop facing an area free of furniture and other
   objects. The Motion Detector should be at a height of about 15 cm above your
   waist level.

2. Use short strips of masking tape on the floor to mark the 1 m, 2 m, 2.5 m, 3 m,
   and 4 m distances from the Motion Detector.

3. Connect the Motion Detector.

   a. Open the pivoting head of the Motion Dectector.

   b. If the Motion Detector has a sensitivity switch, set it to Normal.

   c. Turn on the calculator and connect it to the Motion Detector.
   (This may require the use of a data-collection interface.)

4. Set up EasyData for data collection.

   a. Start the EasyData application, if it is not already running.

   b. Select File from the Main screen, and then select **New** to reset the application.

5. Explore making distance *vs.* time graphs.

   a. Stand at the 1.0 m mark, facing away from the Motion Detector.

   b. Signal your partner to select Start.

   c. Slowly walk to the 2.5 m mark and stop.

   d. When data collection ends, a graph of distance
   versus time will be displayed.

   e. Sketch your graph on the empty graph provided at
   the right.

   f. Select Main to return to the Main screen.

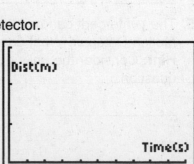

6. Repeat Step 5 while walking faster. Sketch your new line on the same graph.

Holt McDougal Geometry

LESSON 3-6C Parallel and Perpendicular Lines
Technology Lab continued

Try This

1. Describe the differences between your two graphs. _____

_____

Activity 2 Matching Distance *vs.* Time Graphs

1. Set up the calculator and interface for distance *vs.* time graph matching.

   a. Select ⌈Setup⌉ from the Main screen, then select **Distance Match**.

   b. Select ⌈Start⌉ and then select ⌈Next⌉ after reading the Distance Match information.

   c. EasyData randomly generates matching graphs like the one shown here; your graph may be different.

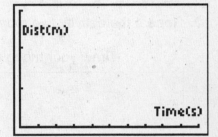

2. Match the first distance *vs.* time graph.

   a. Examine the graph and plan what you will do to match it. Note: The vertical axis runs from 0 to 3 meters. Data will be collected for 10 seconds.

   b. Take your starting position in front of the Motion Detector.

   c. When you are ready to begin matching, signal your partner to select ⌈Start⌉.

   d. Move according to your plan.

   e. Examine the graph of the results.

   f. Sketch your results on Graph 1 below. Describe what you had to do to match the first graph. Sketch the graph you were matching and the graph of your motion.

   g. If you want to repeat the first match, select ⌈Retry⌉. If you are ready to move on to a second graph, select ⌈New⌉.

3. Repeat Step 2 until you have matched a total of three distance *vs.* time graphs.

Try This

Sketch your results in the empty graphs provided below. Describe what you had to do to match each of the graphs.

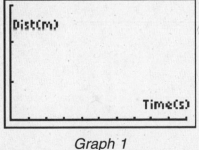

Graph 1

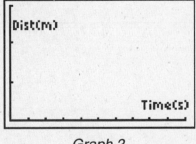

Graph 2

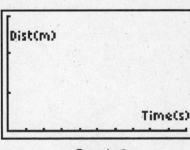

Graph 3

_____   _____   _____

_____   _____   _____

Holt McDougal Geometry

LESSON 4-2 Triangle Congruence

Geometry Lab Recording Sheet: Develop the Triangle Sum Theorem

Use with the lesson Angle Relationships in Triangles

Try This

1. What do you notice about the three angles of the triangle that you traced?

   _____

   _____

2. Repeat the activity two more times using two different triangles.

   Draw your triangle.   Draw your triangle.

   Do you get the same results each time? _____

3. Write an equation describing the relationship among the measures of the angles of △ABC.

   _____

   _____

4. Use inductive reasoning to write a conjecture about the sum of the measures of the angles of a triangle.

   _____

   _____

Holt McDougal Geometry

Name _____ Date _____ Class _____

LESSON
4-2

Triangle Congruence
Technology Lab

Use with the lesson Angle Relationships in Triangles

Activity
Determine if a triangle is acute, right, or obtuse using the graphing calculator.

Begin by pressing `APPS`. Scroll down to **GeoMastr** and press
`ENTER`. Press `WINDOW` twice and scroll down to **5:Triangle** and press `ENTER`.
To draw a triangle you must move the cursor to three different
coordinate points. Use the arrow keys
to move the cursor to (0, 0) and press
`ENTER`. Move the cursor to (25, 0)
and press `ENTER`. Move the
cursor to (15, 19) and press `ENTER`
twice.

Press `TRACE` `ZOOM` to reach the Measure
menu and scroll to **3: Angle** and press
`ENTER`.

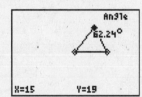

Move the cursor to (0, 0) and press `ENTER`.
To find the measure of the angle at vertex (25, 0),
move the cursor to this point and press `ENTER`.

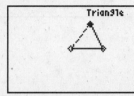

Finally, move the cursor to last vertex, (15, 19)
and press `ENTER`. The angle measure 62.24°
will appear on the screen.

Use the same procedure to find the angle measures of the other two angles.

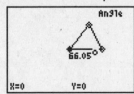 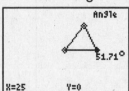

Because all three angles are less than 90°, the triangle is acute.

35

Holt McDougal Geometry

LESSON
4-2
Triangle Congruence
Technology Lab continued

Try This
Plot the points and draw each triangle on a graphing calculator. Then, determine if each triangle is acute, right, or obtuse. Give the angle measure for each angle.

1. (12, 2), (−19, −3), (−16, 23)   Sketch:

_____

_____

2. (0, −1), (15, 14), (−13, 2)   Sketch:

_____

_____

3. (−20, 8), (33, 31), (0, −2)   Sketch:

_____

_____

Holt McDougal Geometry

LESSON 4-4

Triangle Congruence

Geometry Lab Recording Sheet: Explore SSS and SAS Triangle Congruence

Use with the lesson Triangle Congruence: SSS and SAS

Try This

Activity 1
Try This

1. Repeat Activity 1 using side lengths of your choice.

Are your results the same? _____

2. Do you think it is possible to make two triangles that have the same side lengths

   but that are not congruent? _____

   Why or why not? _____

3. How does your answer to Problem 2 provide a shortcut for proving triangles congruent?

   _____

4. Complete the following conjecture based on your results. Two triangles are congruent if?

   _____

Activity 2
Try This

5. Repeat Activity 2 using side lengths and an angle measure of your choice.

Holt McDougal Geometry

Name _____ Date _____ Class _____

LESSON **Triangle Congruence**
4-4 *Geometry Lab Recording Sheet: Explore SSS and SAS Triangle Congruence* continued

Are your results the same? _____

6. Suppose you know two side lengths of a triangle and the measure of the angle between these sides. Can the length of the third side be any measure?

_____

Explain.

_____

7. How does your answer to Problem 6 provide a shortcut for proving triangles congruent?

_____

8. Use the two given sides and the given angle from Activity 2 to form a triangle that is not congruent to the triangle you formed. (*Hint:* One of the given sides does not have to be adjacent to the given angle.)

9. Complete the following conjecture based on your results. Two triangles are congruent if

_____

38 **Holt McDougal Geometry**

Triangle Congruence

LESSON 4-4

Geometry Lab: Investigating Triangle Congruence: SSS and SAS

Use with the lesson Triangle Congruence: SSS and SAS
Materials: MIRA, protractor, ruler and pencil

You can explore what you have learned about triangle congruence with a MIRA.

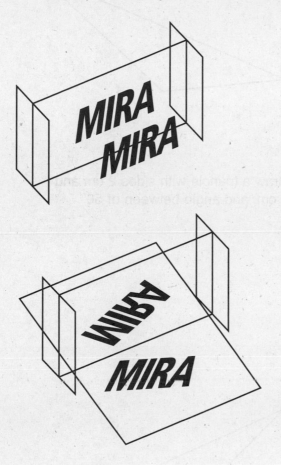

A MIRA is made of red plastic which is translucent making it possible to see both an image reflected in the MIRA, as in the first diagram; as well as an image reflected from paper onto the paper on the other side of the MIRA, as in the second diagram.

The MIRA has a top and bottom. The bottom has a beveled edge, which needs to be placed facing you (and of course, on the bottom).

When you line up the MIRA on a line of symmetry or reflection line, you must place the beveled edge on the line of symmetry or reflection line, and facing you.

When you draw a line you must trace it along the beveled edge.

Activity

Use the MIRA to draw a figure congruent to each of the following figures in the space provided. In the last two exercises, you must first draw the triangle from the information given, then draw a congruent triangle using the MIRA. A congruent figure is one which has the exact same size and shape as the original. In this lab you will explore triangle congruence when you are given the three sides of a triangle, and when you are given two sides and the angle between them.

Holt McDougal Geometry

Triangle Congruence

Geometry Lab: Investigating Triangle Congruence: SSS and SAS continued

Try This

1.

2.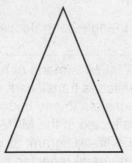

3.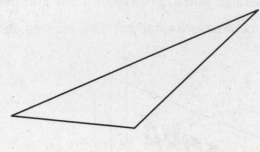

4. Draw a triangle with sides 4 cm, 5 cm, and 6 cm.

5. Draw a triangle with sides 2 cm and 4 cm, and angle between of 50°.

Lesson Triangle Congruence: SSS and SAS

1.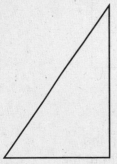

2.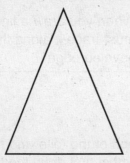

3.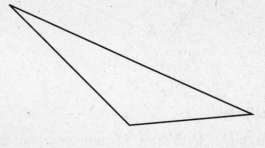

4.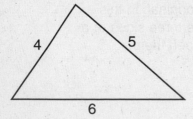

5.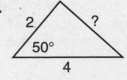

Holt McDougal Geometry

LESSON 4-5 Triangle Congruence

Technology Lab Recording Sheet: Predict Other Triangle Congruence Relationships

Use with the lesson Triangle Congruence: ASA, AAS, and HL

Try This

Activity 1

1. Construct $\angle CAB$, measuring 45°, and $\angle EDF$, measuring 110°.

2. Move $\angle EDF$ so that $\overrightarrow{DE}$ overlays $\overrightarrow{BA}$. Label the intersection of $\overrightarrow{DF}$ and $\overrightarrow{AC}$ as G. Measure $\angle DGA$.

3. Move $\angle CAB$ to the left and right, without changing the measures of the angles. Observe what happens to the size of $\angle DGA$.

_____

4. Measure the distance from A to D. Try to change the shape of the triangle without changing AD and the measures of $\angle A$ and $\angle D$.

Sketch of Construction:

Try This

1. Repeat Activity 1 using angle measures of your choice.

   Are your results the same? _____

   Explain.

   _____

2. Do the results change if one of the given angles measures 90°?

   _____

3. What theorem proves that the measure of $\angle DGA$ in Step 2 will always be the same?

   _____

4. In Step 3 of the activity, the angle measures in $\angle ADG$ stayed the same as the size of the triangle changed. Does Angle-Angle-Angle, like Side-Side-Side, make only one triangle? _____

   Explain.

   _____

Sketch of Construction:

Holt McDougal Geometry

Triangle Congruence
Technology Lab Recording Sheet: Predict Other Triangle Congruence Relationships continued

5. Repeat Step 4 of the activity but measure the length of $\overline{AG}$ instead of $\overline{AD}$. Are your results the same?

_____

Does this lead to a new congruence postulate or theorem?

_____

6. If you are given two angles of a triangle, what additional piece of information is needed so that only one triangle is made?

_____

Make a conjecture based on your findings in Step 5.

_____

_____

Activity 2

7. In Step 4 of the activity, how many different triangles were possible?

_____

Does Side-Side-Angle make only one triangle?

_____

8. Repeat Activity 2 using an angle measure of 90° in Step 2 and a circle with a radius of 7 cm in Step 3.

How many different triangles are possible in Step 4?

_____

9. Repeat the activity again using a measure of 90° in Step 2 and a circle with a radius of 8.25 cm in Step 3.

Classify the resulting triangle by its angle measures.

_____

10. Based on your results, complete the following conjecture.

In a Side-Side-Angle combination, if the corresponding nonincluded

angles are _____, then only one triangle is possible.

Holt McDougal Geometry

Name _____ Date _____ Class _____

Properties and Attributes of Triangles
Technology Lab: Developing and Using the Triangle Midsegment Theorem

Use with the lesson Perpendicular and Angle Bisectors

Activity
Compare the length of the midsegment of a triangle with the length of the base parallel to the midsegment.

Step 1 First draw the triangles whose vertices lie on the points (0, 20), (−20, −10), and (20, −10). Begin by pressing ⬛APPS, scroll down to **GeoMastr** and press ⬛ENTER.

Now, press ⬛WINDOW, scroll down to **5:Triangle** and press ⬛ENTER. Use the arrow keys to move to the cursor to the order pairs that make up the triangle. Press ⬛ENTER each time the cursor is on one of the three points: (0, 20), (−20, −10), or (20, −10).

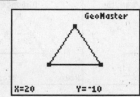

Step 2 Find the midpoints of two sides.

Press ⬛GRAPH and choose **B↑Midpoint** from the Draw menu and press ⬛ENTER. Now move the cursor to the first coordinate (−20, −10) and press ⬛ENTER. Move the cursor to the second coordinate (0, 20) and press ⬛ENTER. Follow the same procedure for the coordinates (0, 20), (20, −10). Connect these two points with a segment. Choose **3:Segment** from the Draw menu. Use the arrow keys to move the cursor to the two previously found midpoints. Press ⬛ENTER twice.

 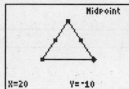 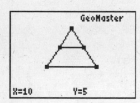

Step 3 Find the distance between the midpoints.

Press ⬛GRAPH ⬛ZOOM to reach the Measure menu.

Choose **1: Distance /Length** and press ⬛ENTER. Choose any point on the midsegment using the cursor and press ⬛ENTER. The length of the midsegment is 20 units.

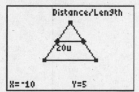

Holt McDougal Geometry

LESSON 5-1A

Properties and Attributes of Triangles

Technology Lab: Developing and Using the Triangle Midsegment Theorem

Step 4 Measure the base of the triangle.

The calculator should still be in **Distance/Length** mode. Use the cursor and move over the first coordinate of the base $(-20, -10)$ and press [ENTER].

Choose the Point in the list and press [ENTER].

Move directly across to $(20, -10)$ and press [ENTER].

The length of the base of the triangle is 40 units.

The length of the midsegment is half of the length of the base.

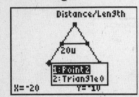 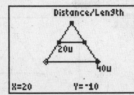

Try This

Graph each triangle on a graphing calculator. Find the length of the midsegment between segments *AB* and *BC*. Find the length of the base, *AC*.

1. $A(-35, 10)$, $B(1, 20)$, $C(28, 10)$

   _____

2. $A(-22, -5)$, $B(-5, 8)$, $C(17, -5)$

   _____

3. $A(-5, -15)$, $B(0, 30)$, $C(5, -15)$

   _____

Holt McDougal Geometry

Name _____ Date _____ Class _____

LESSON
5-1B

Properties and Attributes of Triangles

Technology Lab: Perpendicular and Angle Bisector

Use with the lesson Bisectors of Triangles

You can use your graphing calculator to investigate perpendicular and angle bisectors.

Activity 1
Construct a perpendicular bisector.

Step 1 Begin by pressing **APPS**, scroll down to **GeoMastr** and press **ENTER**. Press **WINDOW** twice and scroll down to **3:Segment** and press **ENTER**. Now, use the arrow keys to move the cursor to the (0, 0) and press **ENTER**. Move the cursor to (19, 11). Press **ENTER** twice.

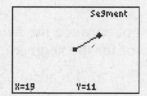

Step 2 To construct the perpendicular bisector press **WINDOW**, scroll to **H:PerpBisector** from the Draw menu and press **ENTER**. Use the arrow keys to move the cursor and pick a point on the line. For example, move the cursor to (14, 8) and press **ENTER**. The perpendicular bisector will appear on the screen.

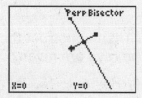

Activity 2
Construct an angle bisector.

Step 1 Begin by pressing **APPS**, scroll down to **GeoMastr** and press **ENTER**. Press **WINDOW** twice and scroll down to **8:Ray** and press **ENTER**. Now, use the arrow keys to move the cursor to the point (0, 0) and press **ENTER**. Move the cursor to the point (20, 15) and press **ENTER** twice. Notice that the ray changes as you move the cursor. To make (20, 15) the vertex of the angle, move the cursor so that it is on this point and press **ENTER**. Now move the cursor to the point (25, −12) and press **ENTER** twice.

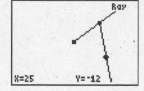

Holt McDougal Geometry

Properties and Attributes of Triangles

5-1B *Technology Lab: Perpendicular and Angle Bisector* continued

Step 2 To construct the angle bisector press **GRAPH**, and in the Draw menu scroll to **I:AngleBisector** and press **ENTER**. Use the arrow keys to move the cursor first to a point on one of the rays, (0, 0), then to the vertex (20,15), finally to a point on the other ray, (25, −12). Press **ENTER** after you have selected each of these points. The angle bisector will appear on the screen.

 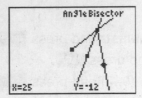

Try This

Use a graphing calculator to the draw the segment between the two given points. Then, construct the perpendicular bisector for the segment.

1. (6, 15) and (−18, −20)

2. (−30, 10) and (23, −15)

Use a graphing calculator to the draw an angle. Then construct the angle bisector. The coordinates of the endpoints on the rays are given.

3. Ray *A*: (5, 5) and (28, 30)

Ray *B*: (5, 5) and (10, −10)

4. Ray *A*: (−15, 25) and (0, 0)

Ray *B*: (−15, 25) and (−20, −15)

Holt McDougal Geometry

Properties and Attributes of Triangles

LESSON 5-2 *Technology Lab: Bisectors of Triangles*

Use with the lesson Medians and Altitudes of Triangles
You can use your graphing calculator to study bisectors of triangles.

Activity 1
Create an inscribed circle using angle bisectors.

Begin by pressing APPS and scroll down to **GeoMastr**. Press ENTER.
Press WINDOW twice and scroll down to **5:Triangle** and press ENTER. Use the
arrow keys to move the cursor to the following coordinate points: (0, 25),
(−30, −20), and (40, −20). After you move to each point, press ENTER twice.

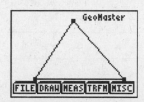

To create the angle bisector of each angle in the triangle, press GRAPH and
WINDOW. Scroll down to **I:Angle Bisector** and press ENTER.
Now, to find the angle bisector of each angle, first move the cursor to one of the
vertices and press ENTER. Then move the cursor to the vertex of the angle of which
you want the angle bisector and press ENTER. Finally move the cursor to the last
vertex and press ENTER. Be sure to find all three angle bisectors.
Find the intersection of the angle bisectors by pressing GRAPH WINDOW
and then scrolling down to **C:Intersection**. Press ENTER.
Move the cursor to a point on one of the angle bisectors and press ENTER.
Move the cursor to a point on one of the other angle bisectors and press ENTER.
The intersection point will appear on the screen.

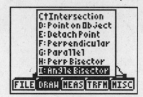
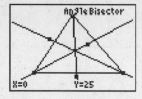
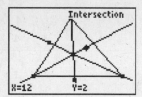

Now, create a circle using the intersection point as the center. Press GRAPH
WINDOW and select **4:Circle**. Press ENTER. Move the cursor to the intersection
point of the angle bisectors and press ENTER. Use the right arrow key to
increase the radius of the circle. Press the right arrow key until the edge of
the circle aligns with the side of the triangle.

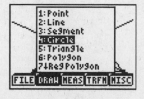
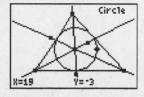

47

Holt McDougal Geometry

Name _____ Date _____ Class _____

LESSON 5-2

Properties and Attributes of Triangles
Technology Lab: Bisectors of Triangles continued

Try This
Draw each polygon using the regular polygon command. Then, create the inscribed circle for each polygon using angle bisectors.

1. (0, 0) square

2. (0, 0) pentagon

3. (0, 0) hexagon

Holt McDougal Geometry

Properties and Attributes of Triangles

LESSON 5-3

Technology Lab Recording Sheet: Special Points in Triangles

For use with the lesson Medians and Altitudes of Triangles

Try This

1. Which three points of concurrency lie on the Euler line?

   _____

   _____

   _____

2. **Make a Conjecture** Which point on the Euler line is always between the two?

   _____

   Measure the distances between the points. Make a conjecture about the
   relationship of the distances between these three points.

   _____

   _____

   _____

   _____

3. **Make a Conjecture** Move a vertex of the triangle until all four points of
   concurrency are collinear.

   In what type of triangle are all four points of concurrency on the Euler line?

   _____

4. **Make a Conjecture** Find a triangle in which all four points of concurrency
   coincide.

   What type of triangle has this special property?

   _____

Holt McDougal Geometry

Name _____ Date _____ Class _____

Geometry Lab
Bisectors of Triangles

Use with Lesson 5-3
Materials: Posterboard, markers, MIRA or compass and straight edge, pencil and paper

Activity
Work with a group of four to create a poster suitable for classroom display.

Step 1 Select a triangle (acute, obtuse, right, equilateral, or scalene) and each person should draw the same triangle large enough to display on the poster (at least the size of an 8.5 in. by 11 in. piece of paper). You will need four triangles. However, do not draw it on the poster yet.
Step 2 Working together on one triangle find the incenter.
Step 3 Working together on one triangle find the circumcenter.
Step 4 Working together on one triangle find the orthocenter.
Step 5 Working together on one triangle find the centroid.
Step 6 On the poster draw the four triangles. Show and explain how you located each of these "centers." There are different ways to find each of these centers. You may use a MIRA, straightedge and compass or any method that your teacher approves.

Here are definitions to help you get started:

Incenter—is the point that is the center of the circle that is inscribed in the triangle. It is the intersection of the angle bisectors of the three angles of the triangle.

Circumcenter—is the point that is the center of the circle that is circumscribed about the triangle. It is the intersection of the perpendicular bisectors of the sides of the triangle.

Orthocenter—is the point of intersection of the three altitudes of the triangle. Note that the orthocenter is inside the triangle if it is an acute triangle, and outside the triangle if it is an obtuse triangle.

Centroid—is the point that is the center of the mass (center of gravity) of the triangle. It is the intersection of the three medians of the triangle. Theoretically, if you placed a pin on this point the triangle should balance.

Holt McDougal Geometry

LESSON 5-5

Properties and Attributes of Triangles

Geometry Lab Recording Sheet: Explore Triangle Inequalities

For use with the lesson Indirect Proof and Inequalities in One Triangle

Try This

Activity 1

1. Draw a large scalene triangle. Label the vertices *A*, *B*, and *C*.

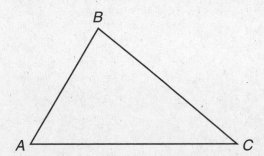

2. Measure the sides and the angles. Copy the table below and record the measures in the first row.

Triangle	BC	AC	AB	m∠A	m∠B	m∠C
1						
2						
3						
4						

Try This

1. In the table, draw a circle around the longest side length, and draw a circle at the greatest angle measure of △*ABC*. Draw a square around the shortest side length, and draw a square around the least angle measure.

2. Make a Conjecture Where is the longest side in relation to the largest angle?

_____

Where is the shortest side in relation to the smallest angle?

_____

Holt McDougal Geometry

Properties and Attributes of Triangles

Geometry Lab Recording Sheet: Explore Triangle Inequalities continued

3. Draw three more scalene triangles and record the measures in the table.

Does your conjecture hold? _____

Activity 2

1. Cut three sets of straws to the following lengths.

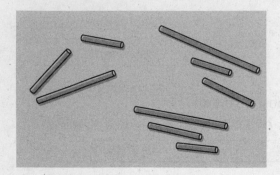

3 inches, 4 inches, 6 inches

3 inches, 4 inches, 7 inches

3 inches, 4 inches, 8 inches

2. Try to make a triangle with each set of straws.

Try This

4. Which sets of chenille stems make a triangle? _____

5. Make a Conjecture For each set of chenille stems, compare the sum of any two lengths with the third length. What is the relationship?

_____

_____

_____

_____

_____

6. Select a different set of three lengths and test your conjecture. Are you correct?

_____

Holt McDougal Geometry

Properties and Attributes of Triangles

Geometry Lab Recording Sheet: Hands-On Proof of the Pythagorean Theorem

For use with the lesson The Pythagorean Theorem

Try This

Activity 1

1. Draw a large scalene right triangle on graph paper. Draw three copies of the triangle. On each triangle, label the shorter leg *a*, the longer leg *b*, and the hypotenuse *c*.

2. Draw a square with side length *b* − *a*. Label each side of the square.

3. Cut out the five figures. Arrange them to make the composite figure shown at right.

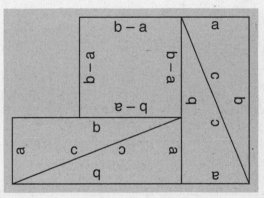

4. You can think of this composite figure as being made of the two squares outlined in red. What are the side length and area of the small red

    square? _____ of the large red square? _____

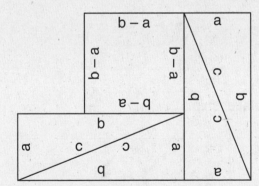

5. Use your results from Step 4 to write an algebraic expression for the area of the composite figure.

_____

Properties and Attributes of Triangles
Geometry Lab Recording Sheet: Hands-On Proof of the Pythagorean Theorem continued

6. Now rearrange the five figures to make a single square with side length *c*. Write an algebraic expression for the area of this square.

_____

Try This

1. Since the composite figure and the square with side length *c* are made of the same five shapes, their areas are equal.

Write and simplify an equation to represent this relationship.

_____

What conclusion can you make?

_____

2. Draw a scalene right angle with different side lengths. Repeat the activity

Write and simplify an equation to represent this relationship.

_____

Do you reach the same conclusion?

_____

Holt McDougal Geometry

Properties and Attributes of Triangles

LESSON 5-7 *Technology Lab: Pythagorean Theorem*

Use with the lesson The Pythagorean Theorem

Activity

Use the area of squares with side lengths 15, 20, and 25 units to determine if the triangle created is a right triangle.

Begin by pressing APPS scroll down to **GeoMastr** and press ENTER. Press WINDOW twice and scroll down to **6:Polygon** and press ENTER.

• Move the cursor to each of the following points and press ENTER twice after each point: (0, 0), (15, 0), (15, −15), (0, −15).

• Follow the same procedure for the second square and use the coordinates (0, 0), (−20, 0), (−20, 20), and (0, 20).

• Create a third square using the coordinates (40, 0), (40, 25), (15, 25), and (15, 0).

Now press GRAPH TRACE and choose **3:Rotation**.
Move the cursor to a point on the largest square and press ENTER.
Now, move the cursor to the point (15, 0) as the point of rotation and press ENTER. Use the + key to rotate the square until the point (15, 25) has been rotated to the point (0, 20).

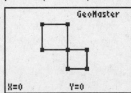 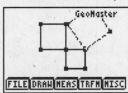

Now press GRAPH ZOOM and choose **2:Area** and press ENTER.
Pick a coordinate within the square approximately touching one of its side such as (19, 3) and press ENTER.

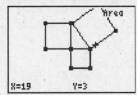 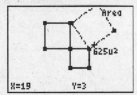

Follow the same procedure to find the area of the two other squares.

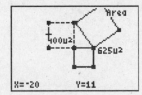 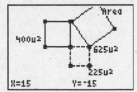

Since the sum of the areas of the two smaller squares is the same as the area of the larger square, the triangle created is a right triangle.

Holt McDougal Geometry

LESSON
5-7

Properties and Attributes of Triangles

Technology Lab: Pythagorean Theorem continued

Try This

Use the given coordinates to draw three different squares. Then, use the rotation tool on your graphing calculator to rotate the larger square so that the three squares create a triangle. Then, find the area of each rectangle and determine if the triangle created is a right triangle.

1. Square 1: (0, 0), (0, 12), (−12, 12), (−12, 0)

   Square 2: (9, 0), (9, −9), (0, −9), (0, 0)

   Square 3: (9, 15), (9, 0), (24, 0), (24, 15)

   _____

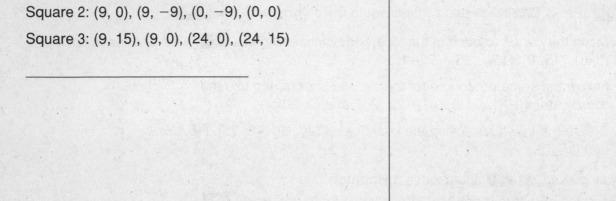

2. Square 1: (−5, −5), (−5, 15), (−25, 15), (−25, −5)

   Square 2: (−5, −5), (−5, −20), (10, −20), (10, −5)

   Square 3: (10, −5), (10, 20), (35, 20), (35, −5)

   _____

3. Square 1: (0, 0), (0, 12), (−12, 12), (−12, 0)

   Square 2: (9, 0), (9, −9), (0, −9), (0, 0)

   Square 3: (9, 10), (9, 0), (19, 0), (19, 10)

   _____

Holt McDougal Geometry

Properties and Attributes of Triangles

LESSON 5-8

Geometry Lab Recording Sheet: Graph Irrational Numbers

For use with the lesson Applying Special Right Triangles

Try This

1. Sketch the two right triangles from Step 6.

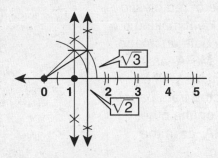

Label the side lengths and use the Pythagorean Theorem to show why the construction is correct. _____

2. Construct $\sqrt{4}$ and verify that it is equal to 2.

3. Construct $\sqrt{5}$ through $\sqrt{9}$ and verify that $\sqrt{9}$ is equal to 3.

4. Set your compass to the length of the segment from 0 to $\sqrt{2}$. Mark off another segment of length $\sqrt{2}$ to show that $\sqrt{8}$ is equal to $2\sqrt{2}$.

Holt McDougal Geometry

Properties and Attributes of Triangles

Geometry Lab: Reflecting Special Right Triangles

Use with Lesson Applying Special Right Triangles
Materials: MIRA, protractor, ruler and pencil

You can explore what you have learned about triangle congruence with a MIRA.

A MIRA is made of red plastic which is translucent making it possible to see both an image reflected in the MIRA, as in the first diagram; as well as an image reflected from paper onto the paper on the other side of the MIRA, as in the second diagram.

The MIRA has a top and bottom. The bottom has a beveled edge, which needs to be placed facing you (and of course, on the bottom).

When you line up the MIRA on a line of symmetry or reflection line, you must place the beveled edge on the line of symmetry or reflection line, and facing you.

When you draw a line you must trace it along the beveled edge.

Activity

You will use the MIRA to draw either a square or equilateral triangle from the given triangles. You will be using the MIRA to reflect the given triangle in such a way that it forms the required figure (square or equilateral triangle) when its image is drawn adjacent to the original triangle. You will be using the MIRA as a line of symmetry (or reflection line).

Holt McDougal Geometry

Name _____ Date _____ Class _____

Properties and Attributes of Triangles

LESSON 5-8

Geometry Lab: Reflecting Special Right Triangles continued

Use these 45°-45°-90° triangles to draw squares:

1.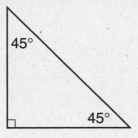

2.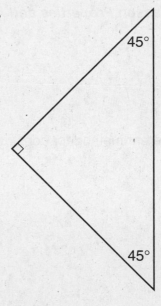

3.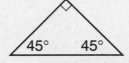

Use these 30°-60°-90° triangles to draw equilateral triangles.

4.

5.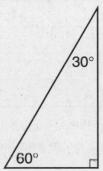

6.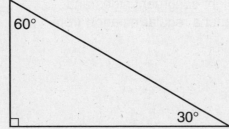

Holt McDougal Geometry

| LESSON 6-1 | **Polygons and Quadrilaterals** |

Geometry Lab Recording Sheet: Construct Regular Polygons

For use with the lesson Properties and Attributes of Polygons

Try This

Activity 1
Try This

1. Describe a different method for constructing a regular quadrilateral.

_____

_____

_____

_____

_____

_____

2. The regular quadrilateral in Activity 1 is inscribed in the circle. What is the relationship between the circle and the regular quadrilateral?

_____

3. A *regular octagon* is an eight-sided polygo that has eight congruent sides and eight congruent angles. Use angle bisectors to construct a regular octagon from a regular quadrilateral.

Holt McDougal Geometry

LESSON 6-1

Polygons and Quadrilaterals

Geometry Lab Recording Sheet: Construct Regular Polygons continued

Activity 2
Try This

4. Justify the conclusion that *ABCDEF* is a regular hexagon. (*Hint:* Draw diameters $\overline{AD}$, $\overline{BE}$, and $\overline{CF}$. What types of triangles are formed?)

_____

_____

_____

_____

_____

_____

5. A *regular dodecagon* is a twelve-sided polygon that has twelve congruent sides and twelve congruent angles. Use the construction of a regular hexagon to construct a regular dodecagon. Explain your method.

_____

_____

_____

_____

_____

_____

Holt McDougal Geometry

LESSON 6-1

Polygons and Quadrilaterals

Geometry Lab Recording Sheet: Construct Regular Polygons continued

Activity 3
Try This

6. A *regular decagon* is a ten-sided polygon that has ten congruent sides and ten congruent angles. Use the construction of a regular pentagon to construct a regular decagon. Explain your method.

_____

_____

_____

_____

_____

_____

7. Measure each angle of the regular polygons in Activities 1–3, and complete the following table.

Regular Polygons				
Number of Sides	3	4	5	6
Measure of Each Angle	60°			
Sum of Angle Measures	180°			

8. **Make a Conjecture** What is a general rule for finding the sum of the angle measures in a regular polygon with *n* sides?

_____

9. **Make a Conjecture** What is a general rule for finding the measure of each angle in a regular polygon with *n* sides?

_____

Holt McDougal Geometry

Polygons and Quadrilaterals

LESSON 6-2 *Geometry Lab Recording Sheet: Explore Properties of Parallelogram*

For use with the lesson Properties of Parallelograms

Try This

1. Use opposite sides of an index card to draw a set of parallel lines. Then use opposite sides of a ruler to draw a second set of parallel lines that intersects the first. Label the points of intersection as *A*, *B*, *C*, and *D*, in that order. Quadrilateral *ABCD* has two pairs of parallel sides. It is a *parallelogram.*

2. Place a second piece of patty paper over the first and trace *ABCD*. Label the points that correspond to *A*, *B*, *C*, and *D* as *Q*, *R*, *S*, and *T*, in that order. The parallelograms *ABCD* and *QRST* are congruent. Name all the pairs of congruent corresponding sides and angles.

   _____

3. Lay *ABCD* over *QRST* so that $\overline{AB}$ overlays $\overline{ST}$. What do you notice about their

   lengths? _____

   What does this tell you about $\overline{AB}$ and $\overline{CD}$? _____

   Now move *ABCD* so that $\overline{DA}$ overlays $\overline{RS}$. What do you notice about their

   lengths? _____

   What does this tell you about $\overline{DA}$ and $\overline{BC}$? _____

4. Lay *ABCD* over *QRST* so that ∠*A* overlays ∠*S*. What do you notice about their

   measures? _____

   What does this tell you about ∠*A* and ∠*C*? _____

   Now move *ABCD* so that ∠*B* overlays ∠*T*. What do you notice about their

   measures? _____

   What does this tell you about ∠*B* and ∠*D*? _____

Holt McDougal Geometry

Name _____ Date _____ Class _____

Polygons and Quadrilaterals
LESSON
6-2 *Geometry Lab Recording Sheet: Explore Properties of Parallelogram* continued

5. Arrange the pieces of patty paper so that $\overline{RS}$ overlays $\overline{AD}$. What do you notice

   about $\overline{QR}$ and $\overline{AB}$? _____

   What does this tell you about $\angle A$ and $\angle R$? _____

   What can you conclude about $\angle A$ and $\angle B$? _____

6. Draw diagonals $\overline{AC}$ and $\overline{BD}$. Fold ABCD so that A matches C, making a crease. Unfold the paper and fold it again so that B matches D, making another crease.

   What do you notice about the creases?

   _____

   _____

   What can you conclude about the diagonals?

   _____

   _____

Try This

1. Repeat the above steps with a different parallelogram.

   Do you get the same results? _____

2. **Make a Conjecture.** How do you think the sides of a parallelogram are related to each other? Write your conjecture as a conditional statement.

   _____

   How do you think the sides of a parallelogram are related to the angles? Write your conjecture as a conditional statement.

   _____

   How do you think the sides of a parallelogram are related to the diagonals? Write your conjecture as a conditional statement.

   _____

Copyright © by Holt McDougal.
All rights reserved.   **64**   **Holt McDougal Geometry**

LESSON
6-2
Polygons and Quadrilaterals
Technology Lab

Use with the lesson *Properties of Parallelograms*

You can use The Geometer's Sketchpad to investigate the properties of parallelograms.

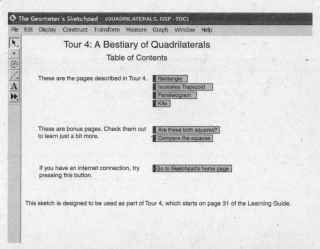

Activity

Step 1 Opening a Pre-sketch.
- Begin a new sketch. Under the **File** menu, go to **Open**.
- Click on **Samples** and then **Tours**.
- Now click on Quadrilaterals.
- Click on Parallelogram.

Step 2 Investigating Parallelograms.

- What do you notice about the side lengths of opposite sides?

_____

- What do you notice about the angle measures of opposite angles?

_____

- What do you notice about the sum of the angle measures?

_____

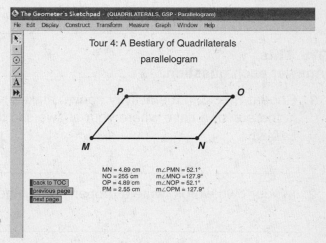

Step 3 Exploring Parallelograms

- Drag point *O* to make the parallelogram lean to the right. Do your answers to the questions in Step 2 change?

_____

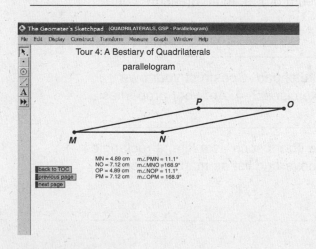

Name _____ Date _____ Class _____

Polygons and Quadrilaterals
Technology Lab

• Drag point *N* to make the parallelogram lean to the left. Make the parallelogram shorter. Do your answers to the questions in Step 2 change?

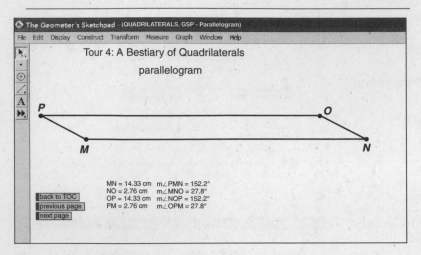

Try This
Answer each question.

1. Repeat Step 3 in the activity above, making various sizes of parallelograms. Is there ever a case where your answers to the questions in Step 2 change? Explain.

   _____

2. In your own words, write a property about the side lengths of a parallelogram.

   _____

3. In your own words, write a property about the angle measures of opposite angles in a parallelogram.

   _____

4. In your own words, write a property about the sum of the angle measures of a parallelogram.

   _____

5. Create a new sketch using The Geometer's Sketchpad. Construct your own parallelogram and test your properties from Exercises 2–4. Are your properties valid for your construction? _____

6. **Critical Thinking** Choose another figure in the Tours such as a kite, a rectangle or a isosceles trapezoid. Repeat the activity above and list as many properties about your figure as you can discover.

   _____

Holt McDougal Geometry

LESSON 6-3 # Polygons and Quadrilaterals
Geometry Lab: Conditions for Parallelograms

Use with the lesson Conditions for Parallelograms
Materials: Geoboard, bands (at least six) and pencil

You can use the Geoboard to explore and discover characteristics about quadrilaterals.

Activity

Some Geoboards have a set of axes pre-drawn on them. If your geoboard does not, then locate the center peg, and mark it as the origin (0, 0). Use rubber bands stretched around four pegs to represent quadrilaterals. For example, place the band around the points (−1, 3), (−5, 1), (−5, −1) and (5, 1). You can locate the midpoints of the four sides easily by looking at the diagram: (2, 2), (0, 0), (−5, 0) and (−3, 2).

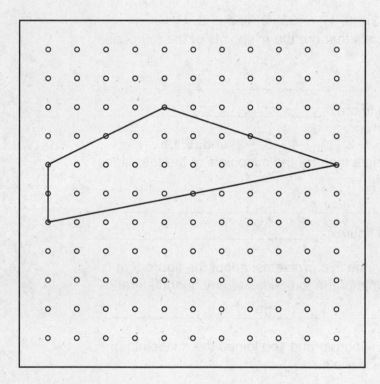

Try This

1. Place a band around the points (−5, 1), (−5, −3), (3, 1) and (−1, 3).
   Place a second band around the points that are the midpoints of the four sides of the quadrilateral.

   a. Write the four midpoints: _____

   b. What is the shape of the second figure? _____

Holt McDougal Geometry

Polygons and Quadrilaterals

Geometry Lab: Conditions for Parallelograms continued

2. Place a band around the points $(-1, 3)$, $(3, 3)$, $(5, -3)$ and $(-1, -1)$.
   Place a second band around the points that are the midpoints of the four sides of the quadrilateral.

   a. Write the four midpoints: _____

   b. What is the shape of the second figure? _____

3. Place a band around the points $(0, 4)$, $(2, 4)$, $(0, 0)$ and $(-4, -2)$.
   Place a second band around the points that are the midpoints of the four sides of the quadrilateral.

   a. Write the four midpoints: _____

   b. What is the shape of the second figure? _____

4. Place a band around the points $(3, 3)$, $(3, 1)$, $(-3, -3)$ and $(-3, 1)$.
   Place a second band around the points that are the midpoints of the four sides of the quadrilateral.

   a. Write the four midpoints: _____

   b. What is the shape of the second figure? _____

5. Place a band around the points $(-5, -2)$, $(1, -4)$, $(5, -2)$ and $(5, 0)$.
   Place a second band around the points that are the midpoints of the four sides of the quadrilateral.

   a. Write the four midpoints: _____

   b. What is the shape of the second figure? _____

6. What conclusion can you draw, from the five problems, about the figure that is formed when connecting the midpoints of the four sides of any quadrilateral?

   _____

7. **Critical Thinking** If you had a parallelogram and you joined the midpoints of the four sides, what figure would you have?

   _____

Holt McDougal Geometry

Name _____ Date _____ Class _____

Polygons and Quadrilaterals

LESSON 6-4

Geometry Lab: Using Tangrams to Study Properties of Rectangles, Rhombuses and Squares

Use with the Properties of Special Parallelograms
Materials: Tangrams (or scissors to cut the ones provided), paper to draw answers and pencil

Tangrams originated in China and were puzzles for creating shapes of animals and objects. The original name, translated from Chinese, is "seven clever piece picture". It is not clear how and where it changed to tangram. There are three stories. 1. The first part of the name may be derived from the Tang Dynasty and the second part from the word "gram" to draw. 2. Named after the Tanka people of China who traded with the westerners. 3. From the obsolete English word tramgram meaning "puzzle or trinket." Tangrams have been used extensively to study the properties of polygons. You will use tangrams to explore quadrilaterals.

Use tangrams provided by your teacher or cut out the ones provided here. You may rotate and flip over tangrams however you need to be able to form the figures. Tangrams must lay adjacent to each other and may not overlap.

Here's a summary of how quadrilaterals are related:

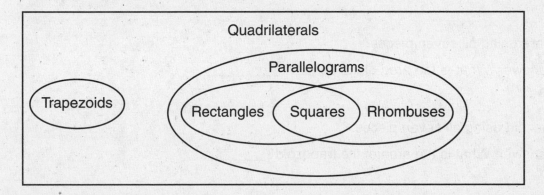

Activity

Work with a partner, each of you should have your own set of tangrams to manipulate. Share your process of creating each figure. Note that there may be more than one way to form the figure. One of the figures is not possible. When you find the one that is impossible, explain why you can not form a square with that number of pieces (hint: calculate the area of the six pieces and determine if it's possible to have a square with that area using the pieces given).

1. Form a square using two pieces—find two possible answers.

   Draw your answer. What is the area of each square? _____

Holt McDougal Geometry

Name _____ Date _____ Class _____

Polygons and Quadrilaterals
Geometry Lab: Using Tangrams to Study Properties of Rectangles, Rhombuses and Squares continued

2. Form a square using three pieces.

   Draw your answer. What is the area of the square? _____

3. Form a square using four pieces—find two possible answers.

   Draw your answer. What is the area of each square? _____

4. Form a square using five pieces.

   Draw your answer. What is the area of the square? _____

5. Form a square using six pieces.

   Draw your answer. What is the area of the square? _____

6. Form a square using all seven pieces.

   Draw your answer. What is the area of the square? _____

7. Form a trapezoid using all seven pieces.

   Draw your answer. What is the area of the trapezoid? _____

8. Form a rectangle (that is not a square) using all seven pieces.

   Draw your answer. What is the area of the rectangle? _____

9. Form a parallelogram (that is not a rhombus) using all seven pieces.

   Draw your answer. What is the area of the parallelogram? _____

Holt McDougal Geometry

Polygons and Quadrilaterals

LESSON 6-4

Geometry Lab: Using Tangrams to Study Properties of Rectangles, Rhombuses and Squares continued

10. Form a triangle using all seven pieces.

Draw your answer. What is the area of the triangle? _____

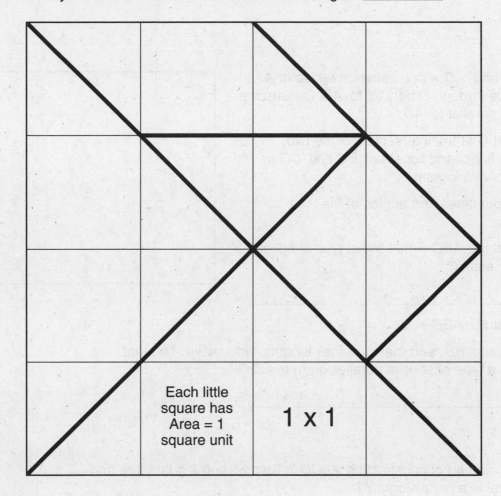

Each little square has Area = 1 square unit

1 x 1

Holt McDougal Geometry

Polygons and Quadrilaterals

LESSON 6-5

Technology Lab Recording Sheet: Predict Conditions for Special Parallelograms

For use with the lesson Conditions for Special Parallelograms

Try This

Activity 1

1. Construct $\overline{AB}$ and $\overline{AD}$ with a common endpoint A. Construct a line through D parallel to $\overline{AB}$. Construct a line through B parallel to $\overline{AD}$.

2. Construct point C at the intersection of the two lines. Hide the lines, and construct $\overline{BC}$ and $\overline{CD}$ to complete the parallelogram.

3. Measure the four sides and angles of the parallelogram.

4. Move A so that m∠ABC = 90°. What type of special parallelogram results?

_____

5. Move A so that m∠ABC ≠ 90°.

6. Construct $\overline{AC}$ and $\overline{BD}$, and measure their lengths. Now move A so that AC = BD. What type of special parallelogram results?

_____

Try This

1. How does the method of constructing ABCD in Steps 1 and 2 guarantee that the quadrilateral is a parallelogram?

_____

_____

2. **Make a Conjecture.** What are two conditions for a rectangle? Write your conjectures as conditional statements.

_____

_____

_____

_____

Polygons and Quadrilaterals

LESSON 6-5 *Technology Lab Recording Sheet: Predict Conditions for Special Parallelograms* continued

Activity 2

1. Use the parallelogram you constructed in Activity 1. Move *A* so that *AB* = *BC*. What type of special parallelogram results?

   _____

2. Move *A* so that *AB* ≠ *BC*.

3. Label the point where the diagonals intersect as *E*. Measure ∠*AEB*.

4. Drag a vertex of the parallelogram so that m∠*AEB* = 90°. What type of special parallelogram results?

   _____

5. Move *A* so that m∠*AEB* ≠ 90°.

6. Measure ∠*ABD* and ∠*CBD*. Drag a vertex of the parallelogram so that m∠*ABD* = m∠*CBD*. What type of special parallelogram results?

   _____

Try This

3. **Make a Conjecture.** What are three conditions for a rhombus? Write your conjectures as conditional statements.

   _____

   _____

   _____

   _____

4. **Make a Conjecture.** A square is both a rectangle and rhombus. What conditions do you think must hold for a quadrilateral to be square?

   _____

   _____

   _____

   _____

Holt McDougal Geometry

Polygons and Quadrilaterals

LESSON 6-6
Technology Lab Recording Sheet: Explore Isosceles Trapezoids

For use with the lesson Properties of Kites and Trapezoids

Try This

Activity 1

1. Draw $\overline{AB}$ and a point C not on $\overline{AB}$. Construct a line parallel to line ℓ through C.

2. Draw point D on line ℓ. Construct $\overline{AC}$ and $\overline{BD}$.

3. Measure AC, BD, $\angle CAB$, $\angle ABD$, $\angle ACD$, $\angle CDB$.

4. Move D until $AC = BD$.

   What do you notice about m$\angle CAB$ and m$\angle ABD$?

   _____

   What do you notice about m$\angle ACD$ and m$\angle CDB$?

   _____

5. Move D so that $AC \neq BD$. Now move D so that m$\angle CAB$ = m$\angle ABD$.

   What do you notice about AC and BD?

   _____

Try This

1. **Make a Conjecture.** What is true about the base angles of an isosceles trapezoid? Write your conjecture as a conditional statement.

   _____

   _____

   _____

   _____

2. **Make a Conjecture.** How can the base angles of a trapezoid be used to determine if the trapezoid is isosceles? Write your conjecture as a conditional statement.

   _____

   _____

   _____

   _____

Holt McDougal Geometry

Polygons and Quadrilaterals

LESSON 6-6 *Technology Lab Recording Sheet: Explore Isosceles Trapezoids* continued

Activity 2

1. Construct $\overline{AD}$ and $\overline{CB}$.

2. Measure AD and CB.

3. Move D until $AC = BD$.

   What do you notice about AD and CB?

   _____

   _____

4. Move D so that $AC \neq BD$. Now move D so that $AD = BC$.

   What do you notice about AC and BD?

   _____

   _____

Try This

3. **Make a Conjecture.** What is true about the diagonals of an isosceles trapezoid?

   Write your conjecture as a conditional statement.

   _____

   _____

   _____

4. **Make a Conjecture.** How can the diagonals of a trapezoid be used to determine if the trapezoid is isosceles? Write your conjecture as a conditional statement.

   _____

   _____

   _____

   _____

Holt McDougal Geometry

Polygons and Quadrilaterals

LESSON 6-6

Geometry Lab: Using a Geoboard to Study Properties of Kites and Trapezoids

Use with Properties of Kites and Trapezoids

Materials: Geoboard, bands (at least 7), protractor, paper and pencil

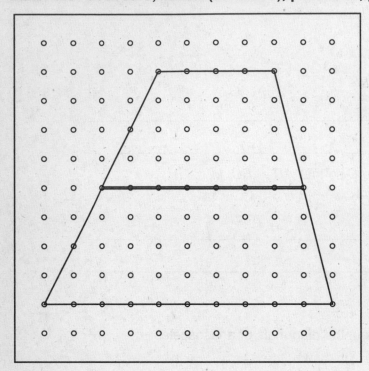

Some geoboards have a set of axes pre-drawn on them. If your geoboard does not, then locate the center peg, and mark it as the origin (0, 0). Use rubber bands stretched between two pegs to represent lines. For example, place one end of the band on the point (−3, 0) and the other end on (4, 0). Use a rubber band stretched around four pegs to represent a quadrilateral. The example to the left shows a trapezoid around the points (3, 4), (5, −4), (−5, −4) and (−1, 4).

Activity – Trapezoid

A trapezoid is a quadrilateral with exactly one pair of parallel sides.
If the legs are equal then it is an isosceles trapezoid.

Step 1 Place a band around the points (5, 5), (3, 2), (0, 2) and (1, 5).

Step 2 Place a band around the points (−1, 4), (−5, 4), (−5, 5) and (3,5).

Step 3 Place a band around the points (−1, −3), (−4, −3), (0, −5) and (−5, −5).

Step 4 Place a band around the points (2, 0), (4, 0), (5, −4) and (0, −4).

These are all examples of trapezoids.

1. In which quadrant is the isosceles trapezoid? _____.

Holt McDougal Geometry

Polygons and Quadrilaterals

LESSON 6-6

Geometry Lab: Using a Geoboard to Study Properties of Kites and Trapezoids continued

Step 5 Clear the geoboard and place a band around (3, 4), (5, −2), (−5, −2) and (−1, 4).

Step 6 Place a band between (−3, 1) and (4, 1). This segment is the median of the trapezoid.

    2. The median of a trapezoid is _____ to both bases.

Step 7 Place a band around (−1, 4), (−1 −2), (−5, −2) and (−5, 4). Place a band between the points (−3, 4) and (−3, −2). Notice that there are three congruent triangles in this section.

Step 8 Place a band around (3, 4), (5, 4), (5, −2) and (3, −2). Place a band between (4, 4) and (4, −2). Notice that there are three congruent triangles in this section.

Step 9 Imagine that you could "move" the triangle for the lower left part of the trapezoid and replace it in the triangle in the upper left, "squaring off" the left end of the trapezoid. Now imagine the same with the right end of the trapezoid.

    3. Write down the points that form the rectangle formed in Step 9.

_____

    4. What is the area of the rectangle? _____

    5. What is the area of the trapezoid? _____

Step 10 Remove all bands except for the ones forming the trapezoid and median.

    6. What is the length of the median? _____

    7. What is the sum of the lengths of the two bases? _____

Conclusion:

    8. The median of the trapezoid is the _____ of the two bases. The area of a trapezoid is the product of the _____ times the _____.

Activity – Kite

A kite is a quadrilateral with two distinct pairs of congruent consecutive sides. The angles between two congruent sides are called vertex angles and the other angles are called non-vertex angles.

Step 1 Place a band around the points (0, 5), (3, 3), (0, −5) and (−3, 3).

Step 2 Use a protractor to measure the vertex angles.

Step 3 Use a protractor to measure the non-vertex angles.

    1. The _____ angles of the kite are _____.

Holt McDougal Geometry

Polygons and Quadrilaterals

Geometry Lab: Using a Geoboard to Study Properties of Kites and Trapezoids continued

Step 4 Place a band around the two vertex angles forming the diagonal. Place a band around the two non-vertex angles forming the diagonal.

Step 5 Measure the angle where the two diagonals intersect.

2. The diagonals are _____ to each other.

Step 6 Measure the length of each segment (cut by the vertex angle diagonal) of the non-vertex angles' diagonal.

3. The diagonal connecting the vertex angles of a kite is the

_____ (two words)

of the non-vertex angle diagonal.

Step 7 Measure the angles formed by the vertex angle and its diagonal.

4. The _____ of the vertex angles _____ the angles.

5. A kite displays _____ along the vertex angle diagonal.

Holt McDougal Geometry

LESSON 6-6 Polygons and Quadrilaterals
Technology Lab

Use with the lesson Properties of Kites and Trapezoids

Compare the length of the midsegment with the lengths of the bases.

Activity

Step 1 Draw the trapezoid whose vertices lie on the points $(-20, -6)$, $(20, -6)$, $(15, 16)$, and $(-15, 16)$.

Begin by pressing [APPS] and scroll down to **GeoMastr**.

Press [ENTER] and [WINDOW]. Select the Draw menu, scroll down to

6:Polygon and press [ENTER].

Use the arrow keys to move to the cursor to the
ordered pairs that make up the polygon.

Press [ENTER] each time the cursor is on one of the
four points: $(-20, -6)$, $(20, -6)$, $(15, 16)$, and $(-15, 16)$.

Press [ENTER] twice after the last point.

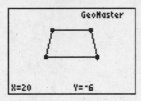

Step 2 Find the midpoints of two sides.

Press [GRAPH] and choose **B:Midpoint** from the **Draw** menu and press [ENTER].

Move the cursor to the first vertex $(-20, -6)$, press [ENTER], move the cursor

to the second vertex $(-15, 16)$, and press [ENTER].

Follow the same procedure for the next two vertices $(20, -6)$, $(15, 16)$.

To create the midsegment, connect the two points with a segment.

Choose **3:Segment** from the **Draw** menu.

Use the arrow keys to move the cursor to the two previously found midpoints.

Press [ENTER] each time the cursor is on one of the points.

Press [ENTER] twice after the second point.

A segment will appear connecting the two midpoints.

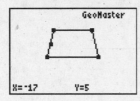 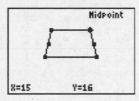

Holt McDougal Geometry

LESSON 6-6 Polygons and Quadrilaterals
Technology Lab

Step 3 Find the distance between the midpoints.

Press `GRAPH` `ZOOM` to reach the **Measure** menu.

Choose **1: Distance /Length** and press `ENTER`.
Choose the two midpoints using the cursor.

Press `ENTER` each time the cursor is on one of the midpoints.
The length of the midsegment is 35 units.

Press `ENTER` again to save the measurement.

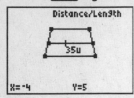

Step 4 Now measure the base of the trapezoid.
The calculator should still be in **Distance /Length** mode.
Use the cursor and move over the first coordinate of the

base (−20, −6), and press `ENTER`.

Choose point from the list and press `ENTER`.

Move directly across to (20, −6), and press `ENTER`.
The length of the base of the trapezoid is 40 units.

Press `ENTER` to save the measurement.
Follow this procedure to find the length of the second base, 30. The length of the
midsegment is half the sum of the bases.

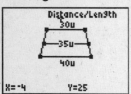

Try This
**Graph each trapezoid on a graphing calculator. Find the length of the
midsegment. Then find the length of the two bases.**

1. $A(-20, -15)$, $B(-5, 10)$, $C(5, 10)$, $D(20, -15)$

_____

2. $A(-40, -20)$, $B(-40, 20)$, $C(16, 10)$, $D(16, -10)$

_____

3. $A(0, 27)$, $B(0, 0)$, $C(31, 0)$, $D(12, 27)$

_____

Holt McDougal Geometry

LESSON 7-2

Similarity

Technology Lab Recording Sheet:
Explore the Golden Ratio

For use with the lesson Ratios in Similar Polygons

Try This

Activity 1

Construct a segment and label its endpoints *A* and *B*. Place *P* on the segment so that $\overline{AP}$ is longer than $\overline{PB}$. What is *AP*, *PB*, and *AB*? _____
What is the ratio of $\overline{AP}$ to $\overline{PB}$ and the ratio of

$\overline{AB}$ to $\overline{AP}$? _____ Drag *P* along the segment until the ratios are equal. What is the value of the equal ratios to the nearest hundredth?

AP = 5.34 cm	$\frac{AP}{PB} = 1.62$	$\frac{AB}{AP} = 1.62$
PB = 3.31 cm		
AB = 8.65 cm		

A ————————————— P ———— B

_____

Measure $\overline{AE}$, $\overline{EF}$, and $\overline{BE}$. Find the ratio of $\overline{AE}$ to $\overline{EF}$ and the ratio of $\overline{EF}$ to $\overline{BE}$.

_____

Compare these ratios to those found in Step 1. What do you notice?

_____

Try This

1. Adjust your construction from Step 2 so that the side of the original square is 2 units long. Use the Pythagorean Theorem to find the

   length $\overline{MC}$. _____

   Calculate the length of *AE*.

   _____

   Write the ratio of *AE* to *EF* as a fraction and as a decimal rounded to the nearest thousandth.

   _____

2. Find the length of $\overline{BE}$ in your construction from Step 3.

   _____

   Write the ratio of *EF* to *BE* as a fraction and as a decimal rounded to the nearest thousandth.

   _____

   Compare your results to those from Try This Problem 1. What do you notice?

   _____

Holt McDougal Geometry

LESSON
7-2

Similarity

Technology Lab Recording Sheet:
Explore the Golden Ratio continued

3. Each number in the Fibonacci sequence (1, 1, 2, 3, 5, 8, 13 ...) is created by adding the two preceding numbers together. That is, $1 + 1 = 2$, $1 + 2 = 3$, $2 + 3 = 5$, and so on. Investigate the ratios of the numbers in the sequence by finding the quotients. $\frac{1}{1} = 1$, $\frac{2}{1} = 2$, $\frac{3}{2} = 1.5$, $\frac{5}{3} = 1.\overline{666}$, $\frac{8}{5} = 1.6$ and so on. What do you notice as you continue to find the quotients?

_____

4. Tell why the following is an example of the appearance of the Fibonacci sequence in nature.

_____

5. Tell why the following is an example of the appearance of the Fibonacci sequence in nature.

_____

6. Determine whether the picture is an example of an application of the golden rectangle.

   Measure the length. _____

   Measure the width. _____

   Is the ratio of the length to the width the golden ratio? _____

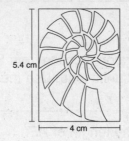

5.4 cm

4 cm

7. Determine whether the picture is an example of an application of the golden rectangle.

   Measure the length. _____

   Measure the width. _____

   Is the ratio of the length and width is the golden ratio? _____

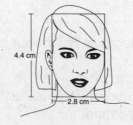

4.4 cm

2.8 cm

Holt McDougal Geometry

LESSON 7-2 Similarity
Geometry Lab: Investigating Ratios in Similar Polygons

Use with the lesson Ratios in Similar Polygons
Materials: Geoboard, bands (at least six) and pencil

You can use a Geoboard to apply what you have learned about similarity.
Two figures are similar if their corresponding angles are congruent and their
corresponding sides are proportional. You will be forming similar figures using the
Geoboard to help re-size the original figure.

Some geoboards have a set of axes pre-drawn on them. If your geoboard does
not, then locate the center peg, and mark it as the origin (0, 0). Use rubber bands
stretched around four pegs to represent polygons. For example, place the band
around the points $(-1, 3)$, $(-5, 1)$, $(-5, -1)$ and $(5, 1)$ to form a quadrilateral.

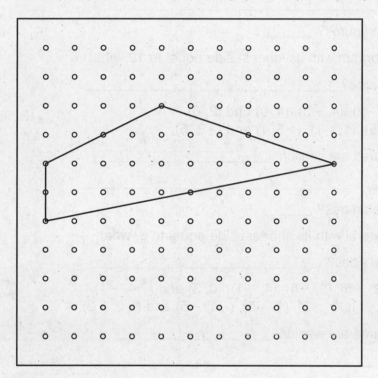

Activity
Step 1 Place a band around the points $(-4, 1)$, $(-4, 5)$, and $(-2, 1)$.
Step 2 Place a band around the points $(1, 3)$, $(1, -5)$ and $(5, -5)$.

1. Explain how you know these figures are similar.

_____

2. What is the scale factor for these figures? _____

Holt McDougal Geometry

LESSON
7-2

Similarity

Geometry Lab: Investigating Ratios in Similar Polygons continued

3. If you had a third similar triangle with its shortest side equal to 5, what would

be the lengths of the other two sides? _____

Try This

1. Place a band around the points $(-4, 4)$, $(-5, 2)$, $(-2, 2)$ and $(-1, 4)$.
   Place a band around the points $(-1, 0)$, $(5, 0)$, $(3, -4)$ and $(-3, -4)$.

   a. Explain how you know these figures are similar. _____

   _____

   b. What is the scale factor for these figures? _____

   c. If you had a third similar parallelogram with its longest side equal to 12, what

   would be the length of the other side? _____

2. Place a band around the points $(1, -2)$, $(4, -3)$, $(4, 0)$ and $(2, 0)$.
   Place a band around the points $(1, 5)$, $(1, -1)$, $(-5, 1)$ and $(-3, 5)$.

   a. Explain how you know these figures are similar. _____

   _____

   b. What is the scale factor for these figures? _____

   c. If you had a third similar quadrilateral with its shortest side equal to 6, what

   would be the lengths of the other sides? _____

3. Place a band around the points $(-2, -5)$, $(2, -5)$, $(4, -1)$, $(0, 3)$ and $(-4, -1)$.
   Place a band around the points $(0, -1)$, $(2, -3)$, $(1, -5)$, $(-1, -5)$ and $(-2, -3)$.

   a. Explain how you know these figures are similar. _____

   _____

   b. What is the scale factor for these figures? _____

   c. If you had a third similar pentagon with its shortest side equal to 10, what

   would be the lengths of the other sides? _____

4. **Critical Thinking** Nina and Willy were working on the same problem to find the
   scale factor of two similar figures. Nina's said the scale factor was 5 and Willy
   said it was 1/5. Who was right and why?

   _____

   _____

Holt McDougal Geometry

LESSON 7-3 Similarity

Technology Lab Recording Sheet: Predict Triangle Similar Relationships

For use with the lesson Triangle Similarity: AA, SSS, and SAS

Try This

Activity 1

3. Measure the side lengths of both triangles. Divide each side length of △ABC by the corresponding side length of △DEF. Compare the resulting ratios. What do you notice?

_____

Try This

1. What theorem guarantees that the third pair of angles in the triangles are also congruent?

_____

2. Will the ratios of corresponding sides found in Step 3 always be equal?

_____

   Drag a vertex △ABC or an endpoint of $\overline{DE}$ to investigate this question.

   State a conjecture based on your results.

_____

_____

_____

_____

Activity 2

3. Measure the angles of both triangles. What do you notice?

_____

Try This

3. Did the construction of the triangles with three pairs of sides in the same ratio guarantee that the corresponding angles would be congruent?

_____

   State a conjecture based on these results.

_____

_____

_____

_____

Holt McDougal Geometry

Similarity

Technology Lab Recording Sheet: Predict Triangle Similar Relationships continued

4. Compare your conjecture to the SSS Congruence Theorem.

How are they similar?

_____

_____

How are they different?

_____

_____

_____

Activity 3

3. Measure each side length and determine the relationship between corresponding sides of △ABC and △DEF.

_____

_____

4. Measure the angles of both triangles. What do you notice?

_____

_____

Try This

5. Tell whether △ABC is similar to △DEF. Explain your reasoning.

_____

_____

6. Write a conjecture based on the activity. What congruency theorem is related to your conjecture?

_____

_____

_____

_____

_____

_____

_____

_____

_____

Holt McDougal Geometry

LESSON	**Similarity**
7-4	*Technology Lab Recording Sheet: Investigate Angle Bisector of a Triangle*

For use with the lesson Applying Properties of Similar Triangles

Try This

Activity 1

2. Measure $\overline{AB}$, $\overline{AC}$, $\overline{BD}$, and $\overline{CD}$. Use these measurements to write ratios. What are the results?

_____

Drag a vertex of $\triangle ABC$ and examine the ratios again. What do you notice?

_____

Try This

1. Choose Tabulate and create a table using the four lengths and the ratios from Step 2. Drag a vertex of $\triangle ABC$ and add the new measurements to the table.

   What conjecture can you make about the segments created by an angle bisector?

   _____

   _____

   _____

2. Write a proportion based on your conjecture.

   _____

Activity 2

2. Find *DI*.

   _____

   Find *DG*.

   _____

   Find the perimeter of $\triangle DEF$.

   _____

3. Divide the length of $\overline{DI}$ by the length of $\overline{DG}$. Add the lengths of $\overline{DE}$ and $\overline{DF}$. Then divide this sum by the perimeter of $\triangle DEF$. Compare the two quotients. Drag a vertex of $\triangle DEF$ and examine the quotients again. What do you notice?

   _____

Holt McDougal Geometry

LESSON 7-4 **Similarity**

Technology Lab Recording Sheet: Investigate Angle Bisector of a Triangle continued

4. Write a proportion based on your quotients.

_____

What conjecture can you make about this relationship?

_____

_____

_____

_____

_____

_____

_____

Try These

3. Show the hidden angle bisector of $\angle E$ or $\angle F$. Confirm that your conjecture is true for this bisector. Drag a vertex of $\triangle DEF$ and observe the results.

_____

4. Choose Tabulate and create a table with the measurements you used in your proportion in Step 4.

Length	Ratios

Holt McDougal Geometry

LESSON 7-6 Similarity

Geometry Lab: Studying Similarity in the Coordinate Plane

Use with the lesson Dilations and Similarity in the Coordinate Plane
Materials: Geoboard, bands (at least six) and pencil

You can use a Geoboard to apply what you have learned about similarity. Two figures are similar if their corresponding angles are congruent and their corresponding sides are proportional. You will be forming similar figures using the Geoboard to help re-size the original figure.

Some geoboards have a set of axes pre-drawn on them. If your geoboard does not, then locate the center peg, and mark it as the origin (0, 0). Use rubber bands stretched around four pegs to represent polygons. For example, place the band around the points (−1, 3), (−5, 1), (−5, −1) and (5, 1) to form a quadrilateral.

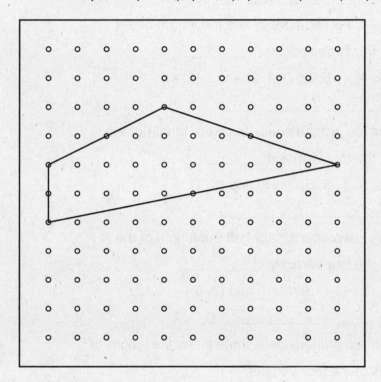

Activity

Step 1 Place a band around the points (−4, 1), (−4, 5), and (−2, 1).
    The figure formed is a right triangle.

Step 2 Form a similar figure whose sides are proportionally twice the length of the original. The coordinates of the three vertices that form a similar figure are:
    (1, 3), (1, −5), (5, −5).

Holt McDougal Geometry

LESSON 7-6

Similarity

Geometry Lab: Studying Similarity in the Coordinate Plane continued

Try This

1. Place a band around the points $(-5, 5)$, $(-3, -3)$, and $(1, 5)$.

    a. What is this figure? _____

    b. Form a similar figure whose sides are proportionally half the length of the original. Write the coordinates of the three vertices: _____

2. Place a band around the points $(-5, 5)$, $(-1, 1)$ and $(5, 1)$.

    a. What is this figure? _____

    b. Form a similar figure whose sides are proportionally half the length of the original. Write the coordinates of the three vertices: _____

3. Place a band around the points $(-4, 4)$, $(-5, 2)$, $(-2, 2)$ and $(-1, 4)$.

    a. What is this figure? _____

    b. Form a similar figure whose sides are proportionally twice the length of the original. Write the coordinates of the four vertices: _____

4. Place a band around the points $(-5, 1)$, $(-3, 5)$, $(1, 5)$ and $(5, 1)$.

    a. What is this figure? _____

    b. Form a similar figure whose sides are proportionally half the length of the original. Write the coordinates of the four vertices: _____

5. Place a band around the points $(1, -2)$, $(4, -3)$, $(4, 0)$ and $(2, 0)$.

    a. What is this figure? _____

    b. Form a similar figure whose sides are proportionally three times the length of the original. Write the coordinates of the four vertices: _____

6. Place a band around the points $(-2, -5)$, $(2, -5)$, $(4, -1)$, $(0, 3)$ and $(-4, -1)$.

    a. What is this figure? _____

    b. Form a similar figure whose sides are proportionally half the length of the original. Write the coordinates of the five vertices: _____

7. **Critical Thinking** Why is near impossible to draw a rhombus on a Geoboard and yet it is easy to draw a square?

    _____

8. **Critical Thinking** What is so special about circles that you would probably never be asked to draw similar circles?

    _____

Holt McDougal Geometry

Name _____ Date _____ Class _____

Right Triangles and Trigonometry
Geometry Lab: Brightness of Light

Use with the lesson Similarity in Right Triangles

The brightness, or intensity, of a light source may be measured with a light meter. In this lab, you will use a light meter to measure the intensity of light at different distances from the light source. The measured brightness of a light depends on the distance between the light meter and the light source. This relationship is an example of an inverse-square law. According to the inverse-square law, the brightness of light at a certain point is proportional to the square of the distance from the light source to the light meter. You will use your results from this experiment to investigate the relationship between the distance and the brightness of a light source and to examine the inverse-square law as it relates to the brightness of light. You will use your data to calculate the square of the distance, and you will analyze the relationship using graphs of your data.

OBJECTIVES

Find the relationship between the intensity of the light emitted by a light source and the distance from the source.

Explore the inverse square law in terms of the intensity of light.

MATERIALS LIST

- small, clear incandescent bulb
- meterstick-mounted bulb socket
- black tube to cover bulb and socket
- power supply
- meterstick
- meterstick supports
- support stand

- clamp for support stand
- CBL 2™ or LabPro® interface
- TI or Vernier light sensor
- graphing calculator with link light sensor cable
- black aperture tube for light sensor
- adhesive tape

SAFETY

- Use a hot mitt to handle resistors, light sources, and other equipment that may be hot. Allow all equipment to cool before storing it.

- If a bulb breaks, notify your teacher immediately. Do not remove broken bulbs from sockets.

- Never put broken glass or ceramics in a regular waste container. Use a dustpan, brush, and heavy gloves to carefully pick up broken pieces, and dispose of them in a container specifically provided for this purpose.

- Avoid looking directly at a light source. Looking directly at a light source may cause permanent eye damage.

Holt McDougal Geometry

Right Triangles and Trigonometry

LESSON 8-1

Geometry Lab: Brightness of Light continued

Procedure
PREPARATION

1. Read the entire lab and plan what steps you will take.

2. Record your data in the data table below.

Distance	Intensity
0.10	
0.15	
0.20	
0.25	
0.30	
0.50	
0.75	
1.00	

Background _____

APPARATUS SETUP

3. The values in the first column of your data table represent the distances at which you will take readings.

4. Set up the meterstick, meterstick supports, light source (bulb and socket), and power supply, as shown in **Figure 1**. Carefully screw the bulb into the lamp socket. Tape the meterstick and its supports to the lab table.

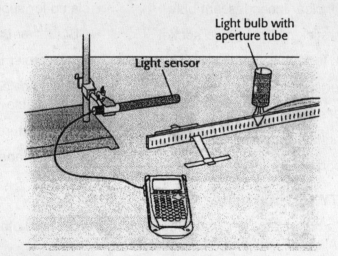

Figure 1

5. Set up the light sensor with aperture, interface, and graphing calculator as shown in **Figure 1**. Set the light sensor directly above the 0.00 mark on the meterstick, as shown.

6. Prepare the light sensor for data collection.

   a. Connect the light sensor to Channel 1 of the CBL 2™ or LabPro® unit.

   b. If your sensor has a range switch, set it to 600 lux.

   c. Use the link cable to connect the TI graphing calculator to the interface. Firmly press in the cable ends.

Holt McDougal Geometry

LESSON 8-1 Right Triangles and Trigonometry
Geometry Lab: Brightness of Light continued

MEASURING BRIGHTNESS OF LIGHT

7. Turn on the calculator, and start the DataMate® program. Press CLEAR to reset the program.

8. Set up the calculator and the interface for the appropriate data collection mode.

   a. Press ◀▶ once to select MODE and press ENTER.

   b. Select EVENTS WITH ENTRY from the SELECT MODE menu to collect light data as a function of distance. In this mode you will trigger the interface to record the light intensity for each position you choose.

   c. Select OK to return to the main screen.

9. On the line below your data table labeled *Background*, record the value for the background intensity that appears in the upper-right corner of the calculator screen.

10. Set the bulb and socket 0.10 m from the end of the sensor. xxxxxxxxxx xxxx sensor clamp and the aperture of the sensor so that the aperture is level, parallel to the meterstick, and at the same height as the hole in the tube that xxxxxx xxx xxxx.

11. Set the power supply at 4.5 V, and connect it carefully with the wires from the xxxxxxxxx xxxxxx xxxxx xxxxx xxxx xxxx xxx xxxx *approved your setup*. When your teacher has approved your setup, carefully plug the power supply into the wall outlet to light the lamp.

12. xxxxxxxxxx xx xxxxxx xxxx xxxxxxxxxxx xxx xxx xx xxxxx xxx press ENTER to collect data for the light intensity. Enter 0.10 as the value of the distance for this trial. Then press ENTER to store this light intensity xxxxx xxxxxxx xxx xxx xxxxx.

13. Carefully move the bulb to the 0.15 m. Wait five seconds, then press ENTER. Enter 0.15 for distance, then press ENTER to store this light intensity-distance data pair.

14. Repeat this procedure for all the distances in your data table.

15. After the last trial press [STO▶] to stop data collection. Carefully unplug the power supply from the wall outlet.

16. Record the data from all the trials in your data table. Use the arrow keys to trace the graph. The *x*- and *y*-coordinates will be displayed as the cursor moves along the graph.

17. Clean up your work area. Put equipment away safely so that it is ready to be used again. Recycle or dispose of used materials as directed by your teacher.

Holt McDougal Geometry

Right Triangles and Trigonometry

LESSON 8-2

Technology Lab Recording Sheet: Explore Trigonometric Ratios

For use with the lesson Trigonometric Ratios

Try This

1. Drag *D* along $\overleftrightarrow{AC}$. What happens to the measure of $\angle A$ as *D* moves?

_____

What postulate or theorem guarantees that the different triangles formed are similar to each other?

_____

_____

2. As you move *D*, what happens to the values of the three ratios you calculated? Use the properties of similar triangles to explain this result.

_____

_____

_____

3. Move *C*. What happens to the measure of $\angle A$?

_____

With a new value for m$\angle A$, note the values of the three ratios. What happens to the ratios if you drag *D*?

_____

_____

4. Move *C* until $\dfrac{DE}{AD} = \dfrac{AE}{AD}$. What is the value of $\dfrac{DE}{AE}$?

_____

_____

What is the measure of $\angle A$? Use the properties of special right triangles to justify this result.

_____

_____

_____

_____

Holt McDougal Geometry

Name _____ Date _____ Class _____

LESSON
8-2 # Right Triangles and Trigonometry
Technology Lab

Use with the lesson Trigonometric Ratios

Use a spreadsheet to find trigonometric ratios.

Activity

Begin by setting up the spreadsheet by
defining the row and column labels. In
this lab, you will be finding the sine,
cosine, sine/cosine, and tangent of
three different angle measures: 25°,
40°, and 80°. In cell A1 enter θ, by
choosing **Symbol** from the **Insert** menu
and clicking on θ. Next, type in the words
$\sin \theta$, $\cos \theta$, $\sin \theta/\cos \theta$, and $\tan \theta$ in cells
B1, C1, D1, and E1 respectively. Now, type in the angle measure in cells A2, A3,
and A4 respectively.

Click on cell B2 and enter **SIN(RADIANS(A2))**.

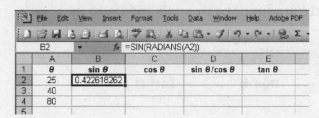

Highlight cells B2, B3, and B4 and press
CTRL D to use the **Fill Down** command.
This will allow you to find sin 40 and sin 80.

Now use the same procedure to find the cosine of each angle measure in
column A.

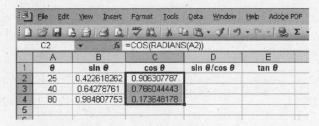

Holt McDougal Geometry

LESSON
8-2
Right Triangles and Trigonometry
Technology Lab

To find the value of $\frac{\sin \theta}{\cos \theta}$, change the formula in D2 to: =SIN(RADIANS(A2))/ COS(RADIANS(A2)).
Use the **Fill Down** command to find this same ratio for 40° and 80°.

File	Edit	View	Insert	Format	Tools	Data	Window	Help	Adobe PDF

D2 =SIN(RADIANS(A2))/COS(RADIANS(A2))

	A	B	C	D	E	F
1	θ	sin θ	cos θ	sin θ/cos θ	tan θ	
2	25	0.422618262	0.906307787	0.466307658		
3	40	0.64278761	0.766044443	0.839099631		
4	80	0.984807753	0.173648178	5.67128182		
5						

To find the value of tan θ, input the formula in E2 to: =TAN(RADIANS(A2)).
Use the **Fill Down** command to find tan 40° and tan 80°.

Notice that the tan θ of the angle measure is the same as the ratio, $\frac{\sin \theta}{\cos \theta}$.

File	Edit	View	Insert	Format	Tools	Data	Window	Help	Adobe PDF

E2 =TAN(RADIANS(A2))

	A	B	C	D	E	F
1	θ	sin θ	cos θ	sin θ/cos θ	tan θ	
2	25	0.422618262	0.906307787	0.466307658	0.466307658	
3	40	0.64278761	0.766044443	0.839099631	0.839099631	
4	80	0.984807753	0.173648178	5.67128182	5.67128182	
5						

Try This
Use a spreadsheet to find the sine, cosine, and tangent of each angle measure in column B.

1.

	A	B	C	D	E
1		θ	sin θ	cos θ	tan θ
2	1	45			
3	2	25			
4	3	60			
5	4	90			
6	5	110			
7	6	335			

2. What formula would you enter in the spreadsheet to find sec θ?

_____

Holt McDougal Geometry

LESSON 8-4 Right Triangles and Trigonometry

Geometry Lab Recording Sheet: Indirect Measurement Using Trigonometry

For use with the lesson Angles of Elevation and Depression

Try This

1. How is the angle reading from the clinometer related to the angle of elevation from your eye to the top of the object you are measuring?

   _____

2. Draw and label a diagram showing the object and the measurements you made.

   Then use trigonometric ratios to find the height of the object. _____

3. Repeat the activity, measuring the angle of elevation to the object from a different distance.

   How does your result compare to the previous one?

   _____

4. Describe possible measurement errors that can be made in the activity.

   _____

   _____

   _____

5. Explain why this method of indirect measurement is useful in real-world situations.

   _____

Holt McDougal Geometry

Extending Transformational Geometry

Geometry Lab: Investigating Reflections
Over the Line y = x

Use with the lesson Reflections
Materials needed: graph paper, straightedge, pencil

Determine the inverse of the graph of the line $y = -\frac{1}{2}x + 4$ by reflection.

1. Graph the line of reflection, $y = x$.

2. Graph the line $y = -\frac{1}{2}x + 4$.

3. Choose two points on the line $y = -\frac{1}{2}x + 4$.

4. Reflect these points over the line $y = x$.

5. Connect these two points with a line.

6. Write the equation of the line in slope-intercept form.

7. Compose the two equations by substituting the right side of the second equation in for *x* into the first equation.

8. Simplify this equation. What equation results?

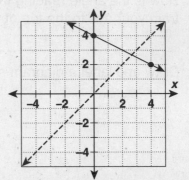

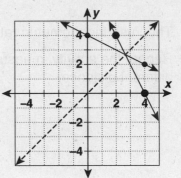

_____

Try This
Graph the equation, reflect the line over *y = x*, and write the equation of the new line.

1. $y = x + 3$ 2. $y = -x - 1$ 3. $y = 2x - 2$

_____   _____   _____

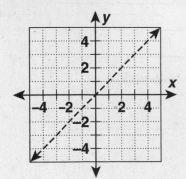   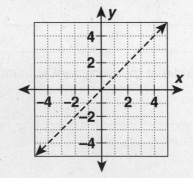   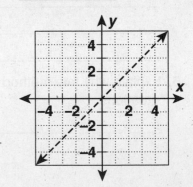

Holt McDougal Geometry

Name _____ Date _____ Class _____

Extending Transformational Geometry
Technology Lab Recording Sheet: Use a Graphing Calculator to Explore Transformations

For use with the lesson Rotations

Try This

Activity 1

1. Graph the triangle with vertices (1, 0), (2, 4) and (5, 3) on graph paper. Enter the point matrix that represents the vertices into matrix [B] on your calculator.

_____

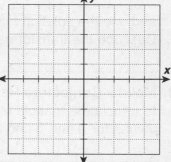

2. Enter the matrix $\begin{bmatrix} 1 & 0 \\ 0 & -1 \end{bmatrix}$ into matrix [A] on your calculator.

Multiply [A] ↓ [B] and use the solution matrix to graph the image of the triangle. Describe the transformation.

_____

Try This

1. Enter the matrix $\begin{bmatrix} -1 & 0 \\ 0 & 1 \end{bmatrix}$ into matrix [A]. Multiply [A] ↓ [B]

and use the solution matrix to graph the image of the triangle. Describe the transformation.

_____

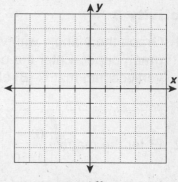

2. Enter the matrix $\begin{bmatrix} 0 & 1 \\ 1 & 0 \end{bmatrix}$ into matrix [A]. Multiply [A] ↓ [B]

and use the solution matrix to graph the image of the triangle. Describe the transformation.

_____

Activity 2

1. Graph the triangle with vertices (0, 0), (3, 1) and (2, 4) on graph paper. Enter the point matrix that represents the vertices into matrix [B] on your calculator.

_____

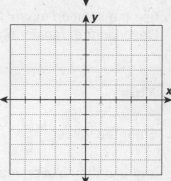

2. Enter the matrix $\begin{bmatrix} 0 & 0 & 0 \\ 2 & 2 & 2 \end{bmatrix}$ into matrix [A]. Add [A] + [B] and

use the solution matrix to graph the image of the triangle. Describe the transformation.

_____

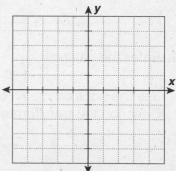

 Holt McDougal Geometry

LESSON
9-3
Extending Transformational Geometry
Technology Lab Recording Sheet: Use a Graphing Calculator to Explore Transformations

Try This

3. Enter the matrix $\begin{bmatrix} -1 & -1 & -1 \\ 4 & 4 & 4 \end{bmatrix}$ into matrix [A]. Add [A] + [B] and use the solution matrix to graph the image of the triangle. Describe the transformation.

_____

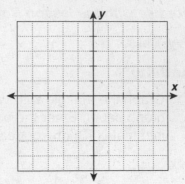

4. **Make a Conjecture** How do you think you could use matrices to translate a triangle by the vector $\langle a, b \rangle$? Choose several values for a and b and test your conjecture.

_____

_____

Activity 3

1. Graph the triangle with vertices (1, 1), (4, 1) and (1, 2) on graph paper. Enter the point matrix that represents the vertices into matrix [B] on your calculator.

_____

2. Enter the matrix $\begin{bmatrix} 0 & -1 \\ 1 & 0 \end{bmatrix}$ into matrix [A]. Multiply [A] ↓ [B] and use the solution matrix to graph the image of the triangle. Describe the transformation.

_____

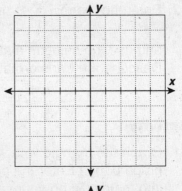

Try This

5. Enter the values $\begin{bmatrix} -1 & 0 \\ 0 & -1 \end{bmatrix}$ into matrix [A]. Multiply [A] ↓ [B] and use the solution matrix to graph the image of the triangle. Describe the transformation.

_____

6. Enter the values $\begin{bmatrix} 0 & 1 \\ -1 & 0 \end{bmatrix}$ into matrix [A]. Multiply [A] ↓ [B] and use the solution matrix to graph the image of the triangle. Describe the transformation.

_____

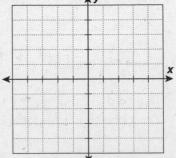

Holt McDougal Geometry

LESSON
9-6
Extending Transformational Geometry
Geometry Lab Recording Sheet: Transformations to Extend Tessellations

For use with the lesson Tessellations

Try This

Activity 1
Try This

  1. Repeat Activity 1, starting with a parallelogram.

  2. Repeat Activity 1, starting with a hexagon whose opposite sides are congruent and parallel.

  3. Add details to one of your tessellations to make it look like a pattern of people, animals, flowers, or other objects.

Holt McDougal Geometry

Extending Transformational Geometry

*Geometry Lab Recording Sheet: Transformations
to Extend Tessellations* continued

Activity 2
Try This

4. Repeat Activity 2, starting with a quadrilateral.

5. How is this tessellation different from the ones you created in Activity 1?

   _____

   _____

   _____

   _____

6. Add details to one of your tessellations to make it look like a pattern of people, animals, flowers, or other objects.

Holt McDougal Geometry

Extending Transformational Geometry
Technology Lab: Creating Tessellations

Use with the lesson Tessellations

Use transformations on the graphing calculator to create tessellations across a plane.

Activity

Begin by pressing [APPS] and scroll down to **GeoMastr**.

Press [ENTER] and [WINDOW].

Scroll down to **7: RegPolygon** and press [ENTER]. Now, input the polygon.

Press [ENTER] at (0,0) and then press the right arrow key 7 times. Press [ENTER] twice.

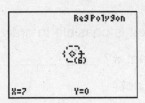

Press [GRAPH] and then [TRACE] scroll to **5: Symmetry** and press [ENTER].

Use the arrow key and press [ENTER] at (7,0).

Choose **2: RegPolygon** and press [ENTER] twice.

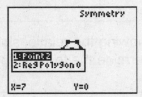

Repeat this procedure but this time choose another point, like (−7, 0). If you continue to do this several times, you will tessellate the plane.

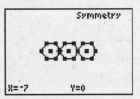
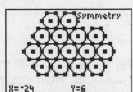

Try This

1. Construct the following tessellation with regular octagons. Use the initial coordinate (−20, −10) and move 17 to the next point. Change the number of sides by using the + key.

Holt McDougal Geometry

Extending Perimeter, Circumference, and Area

LESSON 10-2 *Geometry Lab Recording Sheet: Develop* π

Use with the lesson Developing Formulas for Circles and Regular Polygons

Try This

Activity 1
Try This

1. Do you think it is possible to draw a circle whose ratio of circumference to

   diameter is not π? _____

   Why or why not?

   _____

   _____

   _____

2. How does knowing the relationship between circumference, diameter, and π
   help you determine the formula for circumference?

   _____

   _____

   _____

3. Use a ribbon to make a π measuring tape. Mark off increments of π inches
   or π cm on your ribbon as accurately as possible. How could you use this
   π measuring tape to find the diameter of a circular object?

   _____

   _____

   _____

   Use your π measuring tape to measure 5 circular objects. Give the
   circumference and diameter of each object.

   1. Object _____ Circumference _____

   2. Object _____ Circumference _____

   3. Object _____ Circumference _____

   4. Object _____ Circumference _____

   5. Object _____ Circumference _____

Name _____ Date _____ Class _____

LESSON 10-2 Extending Perimeter, Circumference, and Area
Geometry Lab Recording Sheet: Develop π continued

Activity 2

4. Let P1 represent the perimeter of the smaller square, P2 represent the perimeter of the larger square, and C represent the circumference of the circle. Measure the squares to find P1 and P2 and substitute the values into the inequality below. P1 < C < P2

   _____

5. Divide each expression in the inequality by the diameter of the circle. Why does this give you an inequality in terms of π? Complete the inequality below.
   ___?___ < π < ___?___

   _____

   _____

   _____

Try This

4. Use the perimeters of the inscribed and circumscribed regular hexagons to write an inequality for π. Assume the diameter of each circle is 2 units.

   _____

5. Compare the inequalities you found for π. What do you think would be true about your inequality if you used regular polygons with more skies?

   _____

   _____

   How could you use inscribed and circumscribed regular polygons to estimate π?

   _____

   _____

   _____

6. An alternate definition of π is the area of a circle with radius 1. How could you use this definition and the figures above to estimate the value of π?

   _____

   _____

   _____

Holt McDougal Geometry

LESSON 10-2 Extending Perimeter, Circumference, and Area
Technology Lab: Developing Formulas for Circles and Regular Polygons

Use with the lesson Developing Formulas for Circles and Regular Polygons

Activity

Determine the formula for the circumference of a circle by drawing three different circles on your graphing calculator with GeoMaster and finding the circumference. Enter the data in the table and then use this information to determine the formula.

Step 1 Begin by pressing [APPS] and scroll down to **GeoMastr**.

Press [ENTER] [WINDOW]. Select the Draw menu and scroll down to **4: Circle**.

Press [ENTER]. Use the arrow keys to move the cursor to the center of the first circle, (0, 0). Press [ENTER] and then use the arrow keys to move the cursor to a point on the circle, (8, 0). Press [ENTER] twice.

To find the circumference of the circle, press [GRAPH] and [ZOOM]. Choose **1: Distance /Length** and press [ENTER].

Then choose the circle from the given list and press [ENTER].

Enter this value and the value of the radius into the given table.

  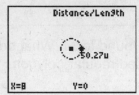

Clear your calculator by pressing [GRAPH] [Y=] and press **5**.

Step 2 Use the coordinate (0, 0) for the center of the second circle and (11, 0) for a point that lies on the circle.

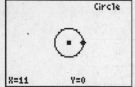 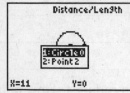 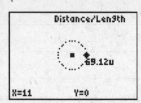

Enter the value for the radius and the circumference into the given table.

Holt McDougal Geometry

LESSON 10-2 **Extending Perimeter, Circumference, and Area**

Technology Lab: *Developing Formulas for Circles and Regular Polygons* continued

Step 3 Use the coordinate $(-10, -10)$ for the center of the third circle and $(10, -10)$ for a point that lies on the circle.

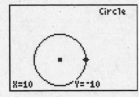 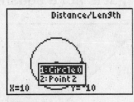 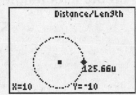

Enter the value for the radius and the circumference into the given table.

Now, find the quotient of the circumference and the radius. When you divide the circumference by the radius you always get **6.28**.

Since $\frac{C}{r} = 6.28$, then $C = 6.28r$.

Circle	Radius	Circumference	Circumference / Radius
1	8	50.27	6.28
2	11	69.12	6.28
3	20	125.66	6.28

```
50.27/8
          6.28375
69.12/11
          6.283636364
125.66/20
          6.283
```

Try This

Determine the formula for the area of a circle by drawing three different circles on the graphing calculator with GeoMaster and finding the area. Complete the table with your findings. Use your data to determine the area formula.

Circle	Radius	Radius²	Area	Area / Radius²
1.				
2.				
3.				

4. The formula for the area of a circle is $A =$ _____.

Holt McDougal Geometry

LESSON 10-3 Extending Perimeter, Circumference, and Area
Geometry Lab: Using Tangrams to Create Composite Figures

Use with the lesson Composite Figures
Materials needed: tangrams

Use all of the tangrams below to create a rectangle that is not a square.

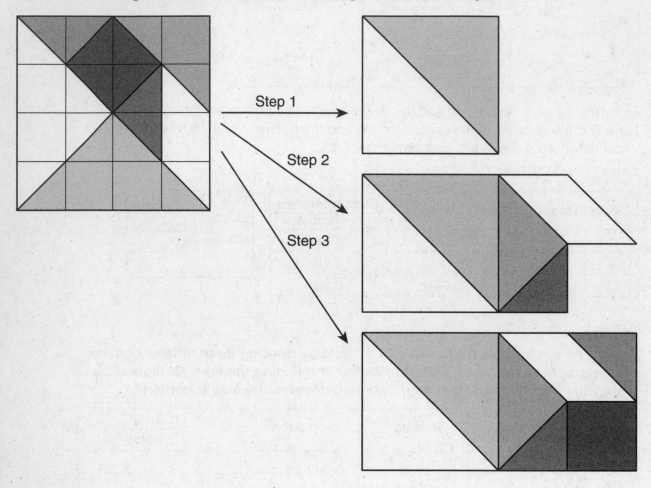

Try This
Use all of the tangrams to create the figures described below.

1. A right triangle

2. A parallelogram that is not a rectangle

3. A trapezoid.

Holt McDougal Geometry

LESSON **10-3** **Extending Perimeter, Circumference, and Area**
Geometry Lab Recording Sheet: Develop Pick's Formula

Use with the lesson Composite Figures

Try This

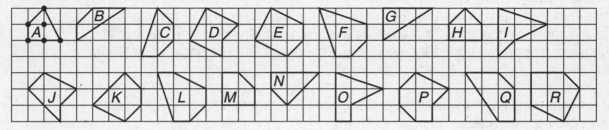

Activity 1

1. Find the area of each figure. Create a table like the one below with a row for each shape to record your answers. The first one is done for you.

2. Count the number of lattice points on the boundary of each figure. Record your answers in the table.

3. Count the number of lattice points in the interior of each figure. Record your answers in the table.

Figure	Area	Number of Lattice Points	
		On Boundary	In Interior
A	2.5	5	1
B			
C			
D			
E			
F			
G			
H			
I			
J			
K			
L			
M			
N			
O			
P			
Q			
R			

Holt McDougal Geometry

Extending Perimeter, Circumference, and Area

LESSON 10-3 *Geometry Lab Recording Sheet: Develop Pick's Formula* continued

Try This

1. **Make a Conjecture** What do you think is true about the relationship between the area and the number of lattice points on the boundary and in the interior of the figure? Write your conjecture as a formula in terms of B, the number of lattice points on the boundary, and I, the number of lattice points in the interior.

   _____

2. Test your conjecture by drawing at least three different figures on graph paper and finding their areas.

3. Estimate the area of the curved figure using a lattice polygon.

   _____

4. Find the shaded area in the figure by subtracting. Test your formula on this figure. Does your formula work for figures with "holes" in them?

   _____

Holt McDougal Geometry

LESSON 10-5 Extending Perimeter, Circumference, and Area
Technology Lab

Use with the lesson Effects of Changing Dimensions Proportionally
You can use a spreadsheet to study the effects on the area of a figure when the dimensions change proportionally.

Activity
Compare the areas of the two rectangles using a spreadsheet.

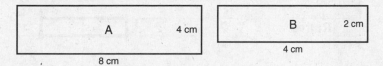

Set up a four column spreadsheet, labeled as shown. Enter the dimensions of each rectangle in the spreadsheet. Then, enter the area formula of a rectangle in cell D2 to find the area of rectangle A.

Use the **Fill Down** command in the **Edit** menu to find the area of rectangle B.

	D2	f_x =(B2*C2)	
	A	B	C	D
1	Rectangle	Length	Width	Area
2	A	8	4	32
3	B	4	2	
4				
5	Ratios			
6				

Enter the formula =(B2/B3) in cell B5 to find the ratio of the length of rectangle A to the length of rectangle B.

	B5	f_x =(B2/B3)	
	A	B	C	D
1	Rectangle	Length	Width	Area
2	A	8	4	32
3	B	4	2	
4				
5	Ratios	2		
6				

Now use the **Fill Right** command in the **Edit** menu to find the ratio of the width of rectangle A to the width of rectangle B.

Note that the rectangles are similar because the length and width of the rectangles have the same ratio.

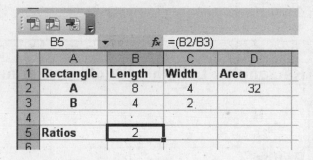

Holt McDougal Geometry

LESSON 10-5 Extending Perimeter, Circumference, and Area
Technology Lab continued

Finally, determine the ratio between the areas of the rectangle by using the **Fill Right** command in the **Edit** menu again.

Although the ratio of the dimensions of the rectangle is 2:1, the ratio of the areas of the rectangles is 4:1.

	A	B	C	D
			fx	=(D2/D3)
	Rectangle	Length	Width	Area
1	Rectangle	Length	Width	Area
2	A	8	4	32
3	B	4	2	8
4				
5	Ratios	2	2	4
6				

D5 fx =(D2/D3)

Try This

Compare the perimeters of the two rectangles using a spreadsheet. Once you have created the spreadsheet, enter the values into the table below and answer each question.

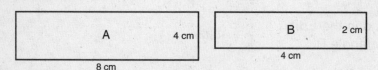

A   4 cm

B   2 cm

8 cm

4 cm

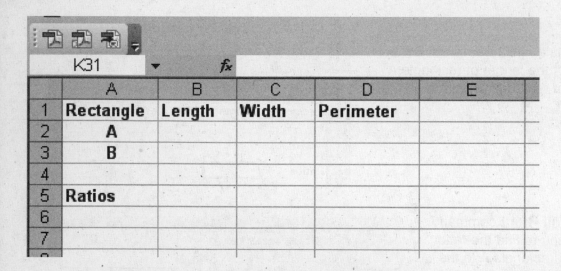

K31 fx

	A	B	C	D	E
1	Rectangle	Length	Width	Perimeter	
2	A				
3	B				
4					
5	Ratios				
6					
7					

1. The ratio between the dimensions of the rectangles is _____.

2. The ratio between the perimeters of the rectangles is _____.

3. **Critical Thinking** When the dimensions of a rectangle are cut in half, the area

   is _____ and the perimeter _____.

Holt McDougal Geometry

LESSON 10-6 Extending Perimeter, Circumference, and Area
Geometry Lab Recording Sheet: Use Geometry Probability to Estimate π

Use with the lesson Geometric Probability

Try This

1. How close is your result to π? _____

   Average the results of the entire class to get a more accurate estimate.

   _____

2. In order for a penny to touch or cover an intersection, the center of the penny can land anywhere in the shaded area.

   a. Find the area of the shaded region. (Hint: Each corner part is one fourth of the circle. Put the four corner parts together to form a circle with radius *r*.)

   _____

   b. Find the area of the square.

   _____

   c. Write the expressions as a ratio and simplify to determine the probability of the center of the penny landing in the shaded area.

   _____

3. Explain why the formula in the activity can be used to estimate π.

   _____

Holt McDougal Geometry

Spatial Reasoning
Technology Lab Recording Sheet: Compare Surface Areas and Volumes

Use with the lesson Spheres

Try This

Activity 1

4. Choose several values for L, W, and H to create rectangular prisms that each have the same volume as the first one. Which has the least surface area?

_____

Sketch the prism and describe its shape in words. (Is it tall or short, skinny or wide, flat or cubical?)

Make a conjecture about what type of shape has the minimum surface area for a given volume.

_____

_____

Try This

1. Repeat Activity 1 for cylinders. Create columns for radius R, height H, surface area SA, volume V, and ratio of surface area to volume SA/V. What shape cylinder has the minimum surface area for a given volume? (*Hint:* To use π in a formula, input "PI( )" into your spreadsheet.)

_____

_____

_____

2. Investigate packages such as cereal boxes and soda cans. Do the manufacturers appear to be using shapes with the minimum surface areas for their volume? What other factors might influence a company's choice of packaging?

_____

_____

_____

114   **Holt McDougal Geometry**

Spatial Reasoning

Technology Lab Recording Sheet: Compare Surface Areas and Volumes continued

Activity 2

2. Chose several more values for L and W, and calculate H so that SA = 112. Examine the V and SA/V columns. Which prism has the greatest volume?

_____

Sketch the prism and describe it in words.

Make a conjecture about what type of shape has the maximum volume for a given surface area.

_____

_____

Try This

3. Repeat Activity 2 for cylinders. Create columns for radius R, height H, surface area SA, volume V, and the ratio of surface area to volume SA/V. What shape cylinder has the maximum volume for a given surface area?

_____

_____

4. Solve the formula SA = 2LW + 2LH + 2WH for H. Use your result to explain the formula that was used to find H in Activity 2.

_____

_____

5. If a rectangular prism, a pyramid, a cylinder, a cone, and a sphere all had the same volume, which do you think would have the least surface area? Explain.

_____

Which would have the greatest surface area? Explain.

_____

6. Use a spreadsheet to analyze what happens to the ratio of surface area to volume of a rectangular prism when the dimensions are doubled. Explain how you set up the spreadsheet and describe your results.

_____

_____

_____

Holt McDougal Geometry

Circles
Technology Lab
Use with the lesson Arcs and Chords

OBJECTIVES

• To understand how to determine the pH of a liquid
• To be able to create graphs comparing pH levels

MATERIALS

T1-84   Unit-to-unit cable
CBL 2™   pH sensor (with DIN adapter if necessary)
Distilled water for rinsing sensor   Beaker or container for rinse water
Beverage samples

IN THIS ACTIVITY YOU WILL

• Pour samples of common beverages into sample cups and use the CBL 2™ with a pH sensor to test their pH.
• Choose a graph that will compare the drinks by their pH.
• Use your results to identify mystery solutions.

PROBLEM

Are most of the beverages you drink each day acids, neutral, or bases?

HYPOTHESIS

Before testing, predict the pH of the beverages.

Before testing, complete the table below to label each beverage as being an *acid*, a *neutral*, or a *base* using what you already know about pH. Predict the rank of each in order of pH (1 = highest acidity).

Beverage	Predicted pH Description (acid, neutral, or base)	Rank (highest pH to lowest)

Holt McDougal Geometry

LESSON 12-2

Circles

Technology Lab continued

Activity
Collecting the Data

1. Collect the beverage samples.

2. Plug the pH sensor into Channel 1 (**CH 1**) on the CBL 2 using the DIN adapter, if necessary.

3. Start the DATAMATE program.

4. The Main Screen is displayed. If **CH 1:PH** is displayed at the top of the screen, go to step 10. If **CH 1:PH** is not displayed, go to step 5.

```
CH 1:PH



MODE: TIME GRAPH-120
1:SETUP      4:ANALYZE
2:START      5:TOOLS
3:GRAPH      6:QUIT
```

4. Select **1:SETUP**.

```
▶ CH 1: PH
  CH 2:
  CH 3:
  DIG :
  MODE: TIME GRAPH-120

1:OK          3:ZERO
2:CALIBRATE
```

5. Select **CH1** and press ![ENTER].

```
    SELECT SENSOR
1:TEMPERATURE
2:PH
3:CONDUCTIVITY
4:PRESSURE
5:FORCE
6:HEART RATE
7:MORE
8:RETURN TO SETUP SCREEN
```

6. Select **2:PH**.

```
▶ CH 1: PH
  CH 2:
  CH 3:
  DIG :
  MODE: TIME GRAPH-120

1:OK          3:ZERO
2:CALIBRATE
```

7. Select **MODE** by pressing 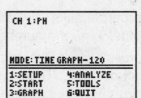 ![ENTER].

```
    SELECT MODE
1:LOG DATA
2:TIME GRAPH
3:EVENTS WITH ENTRY
4:SINGLE POINT
5:SELECTED EVENTS
6:RETURN TO SETUP SCREEN
```

8. Select **3:EVENTS WITH ENTRY**.

```
▶ CH 1: PH
  CH 2:
  CH 3:
  DIG :
  MODE: EVENTS WITH ENTRY

1:OK          3:ZERO
2:CALIBRATE
```

9. Select **1:OK** to return to the Main Screen.

```
CH 1:PH            2.8



MODE: EVENTS WITH ENTRY
1:SETUP      4:ANALYZE
2:START      5:TOOLS
3:GRAPH      6:QUIT
```

Holt McDougal Geometry

LESSON	**Circles**
12-2	*Technology Lab* continued

10. Before measuring the pH of your first sample, rinse the pH sensor as demonstrated by your teacher. Repeat this process each time you are ready to measure a new sample.

11. When you are ready to begin, select **2:START**. The screen displays **PRESS ENTER TO COLLECT OR STO TO STOP**.

12. Place the pH sensor in the sample and gently swirl the container around the bottom of the pH sensor. When the pH reading is steady, press ENTER .

13. The program asks you to enter a value. This value is the number of your sample, NOT the pH value. Type the number for this sample (for example, if this is the first sample, type **1**) and press ENTER . Record the sample name beside the number in the table on the **Data Collection** page. The program returns to the data collection screen, ready for your next sample.

14. Repeat Steps 10 through 13 for each sample, using the number for the sample when the program asks for a value after you have the pH. After you enter the first sample number, the last number you used is displayed at the bottom of the screen.

15. After you have collected the pH value for your last sample, press STO▶ . A plot of your data, or a scatter plot, is displayed, showing the pH value for all of your samples. Use ▶ and ◀ to move to each data point and record the values in the table on the **Data Collection** page.

16. To exit from the DATAMATE program, press ENTER to return to the Main Screen. Select **6:QUIT** and press ENTER .

17. To display the lists showing the results, press LIST . The sample numbers for the beverages are stored in **L1**. The pH values are stored in **L2**.

18. To change the sample numbers in **L1** to the names of the liquids:

    a. Highlight the first element in the list.

L1	L2	L3	1
1	0	------	
2	7		
3	10		
4	3		
5	10		
6	12		
7	4		

L1(1)=1

    b. Press 2nd [TEXT].

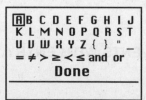

    c. Press ▶ or ◀ to move to the letters in the name, pressing ENTER after each one.

        Note: The first name must be enclosed in quotation marks to tell the calculator that all additional elements of the list will be names.

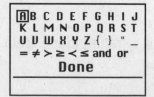

Holt McDougal Geometry

LESSON 12-2 Circles

Technology Lab continued

d. When the name is finished, move to **Done** and press ENTER .

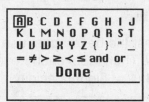

e. Press ENTER again to paste the name in the list.

f. When you finish working with the lists, press 2nd [QUIT] to return to the home screen.

Graphing the Data

Review the pH values on a scatter plot. Record the graphs on the **Data Collection** page. To graph more than seven beverages, use a scatter plot.

1. Press 2nd [PLOT] **4:PlotsOff** ENTER to turn off all stat plots.

2. Press 2nd [PLOT] ENTER to select **Plot1**.

3. Press ENTER to select **On** (to turn on **Plot1**).

4. Select ⌊∴⌋ (the scatter plot) as the **Type**.

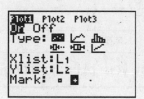

5. Plot the beverage numbers (**L1**) on the *x*-axis and the pH values (**L2**) on the *y*-axis.

6. Press WINDOW to set the window values as shown. **Xmax** must be 1 more than the number of samples. The 0 through 14 for the *y*-range represents the pH scale.

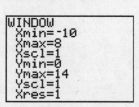

7. Press GRAPH to display the plot. Press DRAW **3:HORIZONTAL** to place a horizontal line at pH = 7.

8. On the **Data Collection** page, discuss the meaning of the location of the points relative to the line.

Holt McDougal Geometry

LESSON
12-2

Circles

Technology Lab continued

Data Collection

1. After you test the beverages, use the displayed scatter plot to fill in the pH values on the table below. Then label each beverage as an acid, a neutral, or a base and rank them in order of pH (1 = highest acidity).

Sample Number	Beverage	Actual pH	Actual pH Description (acid, neutral, or base)	Rank (highest pH to lowest)
1				
2				
3				
4				
5				
6				
7				
8				

2. Display your pH data using a scatterplot.

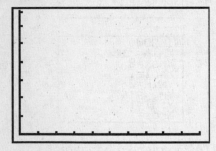

   a. Discuss the meaning of the location of the points relative to the horizontal line at pH = 7.

   _____

   _____

   b. Use your scatterplot to create a circle graph.

   c. Which data display the best job of answering the lab question?

   _____

   _____

Holt McDougal Geometry

LESSON **12-2**

Circles

Technology Lab continued

Try This
Use your data and graphs to answer the following questions.

1. Compare the actual pH rankings to your predictions. Discuss any surprises or differences you find.

   _____

   _____

2. Match each description to a tested beverage.

   Most Acidic   _____

   Most Basic   _____

   Closest to neutral   _____

   Median beverage   _____

3. Give a real-life situation where you could apply these results.

   _____

   _____

4. What is the range in the pH readings? _____

5. Find the mean pH. _____

6. Find the median pH. _____

7. How does the mean compare to the median?

   _____

   _____

8. Which measure would best describe the average beverage:

   _____

   _____

9. Where do most of the beverages cluster on the scatterplot?

   _____

   What does this reveal about most of the beverages you drink?

   _____

Holt McDougal Geometry

Name ______________________________ Date __________ Class __________

LESSON 12-2

Circles

Technology Lab continued

10. Describe how the identity of an unknown solution can be determined based on its properties. How will knowing the pH narrow down the search?

____

____

____

11. Describe the relationship between common chemistry solutions (vinegar, ammonia, and distilled water) and these beverages.

____

____

____

Most of the tested beverages were ______________.

The average beverage had a pH of ______________.

Name _____ Date _____ Class _____

Circles
Geometry Lab: Use Sectors to Find the Area of a Circle Length

Use with the lesson Sector Area and Arc Length
Materials needed: compass, straightedge, scissors

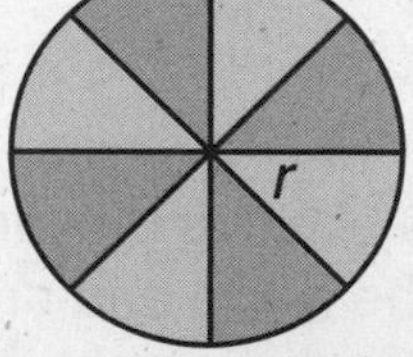

1. Draw a circle. Label its radius *r*. Divide the circle into eight congruent sectors.

2. Cut out the sectors and reassemble them into a single figure, as shown at the right.

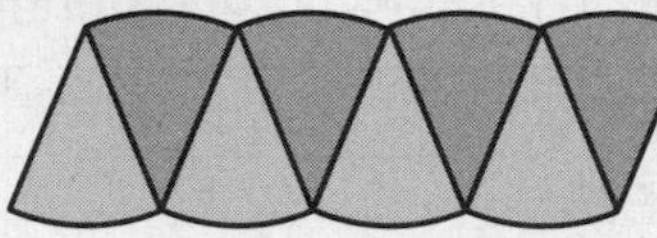

3. If the curved parts of your figure were segments instead of curves, what kind of figure would you have?

_____

4. Divide the circle into 16 congruent sectors by cutting each sector from Step 2 in half. Then reassemble the sectors as in Step 2. As the number of sectors increases, do the curved parts seem straighter? _____

5. What geometric figure do your sector assemblies in Steps 2 and 3 resemble?

_____ The height of your figures is approximately equal to *r*, the radius of the circle. What happens to this approximation as the number of sectors increases infinitely? _____

Try This
Use the activity to answer the questions.

1. The base of your assembled figure is approximately equal to half of the circumference of your original figure. (Why?) Write an expression for the base of the figure in terms of π and the radius, *r*, of the circle.

_____

2. Write an expression for the area of the figure in terms of π and *r*.

_____

3. Why does the method you used in the activity become more realistic as you increase the number of sectors?

_____

_____

_____

Holt McDougal Geometry

Circles

LESSON 12-5 **Technology Lab Recording Sheet: Explore Angle Relationships in Circles**

Use with the lesson Angle Relationships in Circles

Try This

Activity 1

5. Drag *E* around the circle and examine the changes in the measures. Fill in the angle and arc measures in the chart below. Try to create acute, right, and obtuse angles.

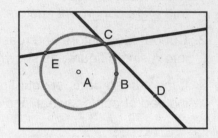

m∠DCE					
m⌢CBE					
Angle type					

Can you make a conjecture about the relationship between the angle measure and the arc measure?

_____

_____

Activity 2

5. Fill in the angle and arc measures in the chart below. Try to create acute, right, and obtuse angles.

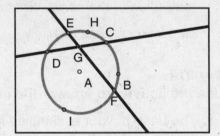

m∠DGF					
m⌢CHE					
m⌢DIF					
Sum of arcs					

Can you make a conjecture about the relationship between the angle measure and the two arc measures?

_____

_____

Activity 3

3. Drag points around the circle and examine the changes in measures. Fill in the angle and arc measures in the chart below.

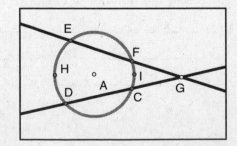

m∠FGC					
m⌢CIF					
m⌢DHE					
number of arcs					

Holt McDougal Geometry

Name ______________________ Date ____________ Class ____________

LESSON 12-5

Circles

Technology Lab Recording Sheet: Explore Angle Relationships in Circles continued

Can you make a conjecture about the relationship between the angle measure and the two arc measures?

____

____

Try This

1. How does the relationship you observed in Activity 1 compare to the relationship between an inscribed angle and its intercepted arc?

____

____

2. Why do you think the radius $\overline{AC}$ is needed in Activity 1 for the construction of the tangent line? What theorem explains this?

____

____

3. In Activity 3, try dragging points so that the secants become tangents. What conclusion can you make about the angle and arc measures?

____

4. Examine the conjectures and theorems about the relationships between angles and arcs in a circle.

   What is true of angles with a vertex *on* the circle?

   ____

   What is true of angles with a vertex *inside* the circle?

   ____

   What is true of angles with a vertex *outside* the circle?

   ____

   Summarize your findings.

   ____

5. Does using geometry software to compare angle and arc measures constitute a formal proof of the relationship observed?

____

Copyright © by Holt McDougal.
All rights reserved.

LESSON **Circles**
12-5 *Geometry Lab: Investigating Angle Relationships in Circles*

Use with the lesson Angle Relationships in Circles
Materials needed: compass, straightedge, pencil

Activity
Determine the relationship between the intercepted arc and the inscribed angle.

1. Draw three different figures in which inscribed angle intercepts an arc of the circle. Include one minor arc, one major arc, and one semi circle.

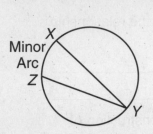
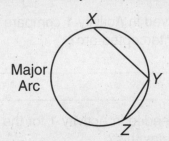
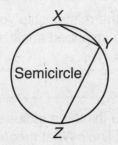

2. Use a protractor to measure the inscribed angle in each figure.

3. Draw central angles to determine the measure of the intercepted arcs in each figure.

4. Enter the measures into the table.

	Circle 1	Circle 2	Circle 3
Measure of the intercepted arc			
Measure of inscribed angle			

5. What is the relationship between the measure of the intercepted arc and the measure of the inscribed angle? _____

Try This
Find the measure of the inscribed angle for each figure.

1. _____

2. _____

3. _____

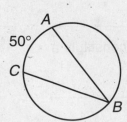
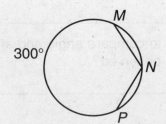
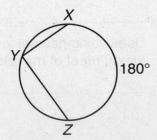

Holt McDougal Geometry

LESSON 12-6

Circles

Technology Lab Recording Sheet: Explore Segment Relationships in Circles

Use with the lesson Segment Relationships in Circles

Try This

Activity 1

3. Fill in the segment lengths in the chart. Find the products of the lengths of segments on the *same* secant.

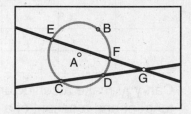

GC	GD	GC · GD	GE	GF	GE · GF

Can you make a conjecture about the relationship of the segments formed by intersecting secants of a circle?

_____

_____

_____

_____

_____

Try This

1. Make a sketch of the diagram from Activity 1, and create $\overline{CF}$ and $\overline{DE}$ to create △CFG and △EDG as shown.

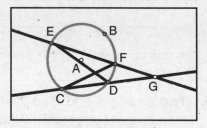

2. Name pairs of congruent angles in the diagram. How are △CFG and △EDG related? Explain your reasoning.

_____

_____

_____

_____

3. Write a proportion involving sides of the triangles. Cross-multiply and state the result. What do you notice?

_____

_____

Holt McDougal Geometry

LESSON 12-6 **Circles**

Technology Lab Recording Sheet: Explore Segment Relationships in Circles continued

Activity 2

4. Measure $\overline{DC}$, $\overline{DE}$, and $\overline{DF}$. Drag points around the circle and examine the changes in the measurements. Fill in the measurements in the chart.

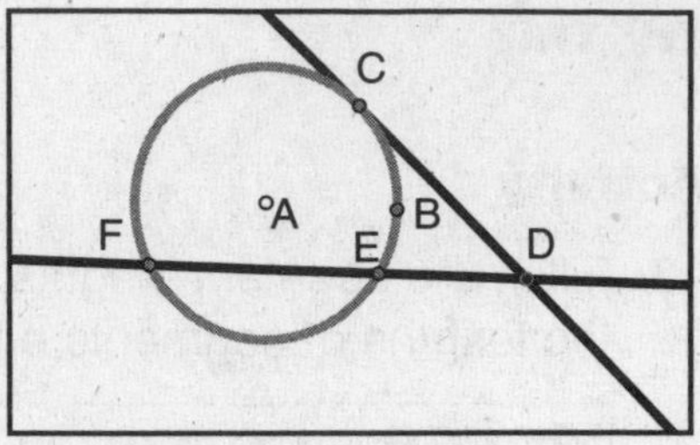

DE	DF	DE · F	DC	?

Can you make a conjecture about the relationship between the segments of a tangent and a secant of a circle?

_____

_____

_____

Try This

4. How are the products for a tangent and a secant similar to the products for secant segments?

_____

_____

_____

_____

_____

5. Try dragging *E* and *F* so they overlap (to make the secant segment look like a tangent segment). What do you notice about the segment lengths you measured in Activity 2? Can you state a relationship about two tangent segments from the same exterior point?

_____

_____

_____

Holt McDougal Geometry

LESSON 12-6 Circles
Technology Lab Recording Sheet: Explore Segment Relationships in Circles continued

6. Challenge: Write a formal proof of the relationship you found in #2.

_____

_____

_____

_____

_____

Activity 3

3. Fill in the segment lengths in the chart. Find the products of the lengths of segments on the *same* chord.

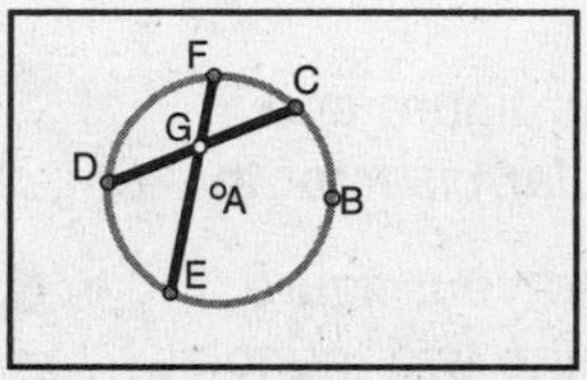

Can you make a conjecture about the relationship of the segments formed by intersecting chords of a circle?

_____

_____

_____

_____

_____

Try This

7. Connect the endpoints of the chords to form two triangles. Name pairs of congruent angles. How are the two triangles that are formed related? Explain your reasoning.

_____

_____

8. Examine the conclusions you made in all three activities about segments formed by secants, chords, and tangents in a circle. Summarize your findings.

_____

_____

_____

_____

_____

LESSON 12-6 Circles

Geometry Lab: Segment Relationships in Circles

Use with the lesson Segment Relationships in Circles
Materials needed: compass, straightedge, pencil

Complete the following construction.

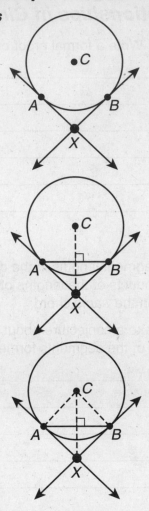

1. Construct ⊙C.

2. Construct two lines tangent to ⊙C from the same external point, X.

3. Measure the lengths of $\overleftrightarrow{XA}$ and $\overleftrightarrow{XB}$.

4. Make a conjecture about the lengths of two segments that are tangent to a circle from the same external point.

5. Add the chord $\overleftrightarrow{AB}$ to your figure and construct the perpendicular bisector to $\overleftrightarrow{AB}$.

6. Add segments $\overleftrightarrow{AC}$, $\overleftrightarrow{BC}$ to your figure. These segments create the two triangles △AXC and △BXC.

7. Because segments $\overleftrightarrow{AC}$ and $\overleftrightarrow{BC}$ are both radii, $\overleftrightarrow{AC} \cong \overleftrightarrow{BC}$.

8. Both triangles share the segment $\overleftrightarrow{XC}$ and $\overleftrightarrow{XC} \cong \overleftrightarrow{XC}$.

9. Because $\overleftrightarrow{XC}$ bisects $\overleftrightarrow{AB}$ it also bisects ∠ACB. So ∠ACX ≅ ∠BCX.

10. Use the information from steps 7, 8, and 9 to make a conjecture about the relationship between △AXC and △BXC.

11. Complete the theorem: *If two segments are tangent to a circle form the same external point, then the segments* _____.

Try This
Use the theorem you found in the activity to find each measure.

1. $\overleftrightarrow{XA}$ and $\overleftrightarrow{XB}$ are tangent to ⊙C and $\overleftrightarrow{XA} = 10$. Find $\overleftrightarrow{XB}$.

2. $\overleftrightarrow{AD}$ and $\overleftrightarrow{BD}$ are tangent to ⊙H and $\overleftrightarrow{AD} = 3$. Find $\overleftrightarrow{BD}$.

Holt McDougal Geometry

Name _____ Date _____ Class _____

LESSON 13-2 Probability
Technology Lab Recording Sheet: Explore Simulations
Use with the lesson Theoretical and Experimental Probability

Try This

Use a simulation to find each experimental probability.

1. An energy drink game advertises a 25% chance of winning with each bottle cap. Find the experimental probability that a 6-pack will contain at least 3 winners.

   _____

2. In a game with a 40% chance of winning, your friend challenges you to win 4 times in a row. Find the experimental probability of this happening in the next 4 games.

   _____

3. **Critical Thinking** How would you design a simulation to find the probability that a baseball player with a .285 batting average will get a hit in 5 of his next 10 at bats?

   _____

Holt McDougal Geometry

LESSON 13-2 Probability

Algebra Lab: Exploring Probability Data

Use with the lesson Theoretical and Experimental Probability

Materials: cardboard to make a spinner, spinner

Activity

There are two types of probability: theoretical and experimental. You will explore both of these in this lab. Theoretical probability is calculated as the ratio of the number of ways an event can occur to the number of total possibilities. For example the probability of rolling a four on one roll of one die is 1 to 6. Experimental probability is based on carrying out an experiment, keeping track of the results and using those results to calculate the probabilities as a ratio of the actual times the event occurred to the number of times you carried out the experiment.

You need to make a "spinner" with six sections. Use a sturdy piece of cardboard or plastic that can withstand your spinning. The spinner should be a circle sectioned off into equally-spaced sections. Color each section red, blue, green, yellow, black, and white. Attach the spinner to the center of the circle or use a pencil and paperclip. Make sure the spinner spins freely all the way around the circle.

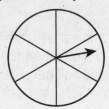

Carry out the experiment by spinning the spinner at least 50 times. More is better! Use the table below and keep track of the number of times that the spinner lands on each color.

Color	Red	Blue	Green	Yellow	Black	White	TOTAL
Tick marks for each color →							Number of times you spin the Spinner:
Total for each color							
Experimental Probability							
Theoretical Probability							

Holt McDougal Geometry

Probability

LESSON 13-2 *Algebra Lab: Exploring Probability Data* continued

Try This

1. Based on your results calculate the experimental probability of landing on each color. (The total for each color divided by the total times you spin the spinner.) Record your calculation in the table.

2. Fill in the table with the theoretical probability for each color (this is the same value for each color).

3. Why do you think the experimental and theoretical probabilities are not equal?

_____

_____

4. **Critical Thinking** If you spin the spinner 200 times how do you think this will affect the difference between the theoretical and the experimental probability of your data? Explain.

_____

_____

5. Create a different spinner, this time with 4 equally-spaced sections. Spin the spinner at least 100 times.
   a. Complete the table.

Color	Red	Blue	Green	Yellow	TOTAL
Tick marks for each color →					Number of times you spin the spinner:
Total for each color					
Experimental Probability					
Theoretical Probability					

   b. How does the theoretical probability compare to that of the experimental probability for each color?

_____

_____

   c. Predict how many times you will spin yellow if you spin the spinner 250 times. Explain your prediction.

_____

_____

Holt McDougal Geometry

TECHNOLOGY LAB 1-2
Explore Properties Associated with Points

Try This

1. Answers may vary depending on student's construction. Students should determine that the sum of AB and BC is equal to the length of $\overline{AC}$. Also, that $\overline{AM}$ and $\overline{MC}$ are congruent and that only one midpoint of $\overline{AC}$ exists.

2. Answers may vary depending on student's construction; No AD + DC does not equal AC; D must be between A and C.

GEOMETRY LAB 1-2
Measuring Lines Using Customary and Metric Rulers

Try This

1. $2\frac{1}{4}$ in.; 5.5 cm

2. $\frac{5}{8}$ in.; 1.5 cm

3. $\frac{7}{8}$ in.; 2 cm

4. $1\frac{7}{8}$ in.; 5 cm

5. $5\frac{1}{8}$ in.; 13 cm

6. $2\frac{5}{8}$ in.; 6.5 cm

7. $\frac{7}{8}$ in.; 2 cm

8. Lines 3 and 7 both have the same measure, so they are congruent segments.

GEOMETRY LAB 1-3
Index Card Protractor

Try This

1. Acute; 30°

2. Right; 90°

3. Obtuse; 135°

4. Acute; 60°

5. Right; 90°

6. Acute; 45°

GEOMETRY LAB 1-5A
Using Models to Justify Area and Perimeter Formulas

Activity

2. AB = 10 units; CD = 10 units
   BC = 4 units; DA = 4 units

3. 28 units

4. 28 units

5. Yes; yes

Try This

1. By counting the squares within ABCD, the area is 40 square units. Let AB equal ℓ. So ℓ = 10. Let BC equal w. So w = 4. The formula for the area of a rectangle is $A = \ell w$. Substitute the known values into the formula and solve for A. $A = \ell w = 10(4) = 40$ square units. Both methods result in the same answer.

2. Calculations will vary depending on student's drawing, but student should prove that the area of a square, A, equals the sides squared, $A = s^2$ and the perimeter is 4 times the side length, or $P = 4s$.

3. Since △ADC is one-half of rectangle ABCD, the area for the triangle is one-half the area of a rectangle, or $\frac{1}{2}bh$ (where b has the same measure as ℓ and h has the same measure as w).

Holt McDougal Geometry

GEOMETRY LAB 1-5B
Area of a Rectangle

Activity

1. Answers will vary but should include rectangles with an area of 32 square units.

3. 66 units; 36 units; 24 units

4. The areas are all the same.

5. 4-by-8 or 8-by-4 rectangle

Try This

1. 1×16; 2×8; 4×4; 8×2; 16×1

2. 1×25; 5×5; 25×1

1. 1×36; 2×18; 3×12; 4×9; 6×6; 36×1; 18×2; 12×3; 9×4

2. equal

TECHNOLOGY LAB 1-7
Explore Transformations with Geometry Software

Activity 1

4. They appear to be congruent.

5. The triangles move together and stay the same size and shape.

Try This

1. The image of the triangle moves in the same direction as the endpoint.

2. The triangles move together and remain a fixed distance apart.

3. Each measurement is the same for the preimage and image triangles. The triangles appear to be congruent.

Holt McDougal Geometry

GEOMETRY LAB 2-3
Solve Logic Puzzles

1. because no one else can own the bird and Fiona owns only 1 pet.

2. Ally and Kian; Emily and Jude; Misha and Danny; Tracy and Frank

3. WG and GC; because the wolf will eat the goat and the goat will eat the cabbage

4. 2; 7

5. Possible answer: You can see all solutions instead of just 1 possible solution.

6.

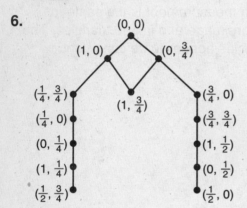

Possible answer: Fill the 1 c cup. Pour the contents into the $\frac{3}{4}$ c cup. Empty the $\frac{3}{4}$ c cup so you have $\frac{1}{4}$ c in the larger cup. Transfer this to the $\frac{3}{4}$ c cup, and fill the 1 c cup. Use the contents of the 1 c cup to fill the $\frac{3}{4}$ c cup, leaving $\frac{1}{2}$ c in the 1 c cup.

GEOMETRY LAB 2-4
Creating Booklets of BiConditional Statements

Try This

1. Square
   Definition: a figure having four equal sides and four right angles
   Biconditional: A figure is a square if and only if it has four equal sides and four right angles

Conditional: If a figure is a square, then it has four equal sides and four right angles (T)
Converse: If a figure has four equal sides and four right angles, then it is a square (T)
Hexagon
Definition: a figure having six sides
Biconditional: A figure is a hexagon if and only if it has six sides
Conditional: If a figure is a hexagon, then it has 6 sides (T)
Converse: If a figure has 6 sides, then it is a hexagon (T)

2. Queen
   Definition: the wife of a king
   Biconditional: A woman is a queen if and only if she is married to a king
   Conditional: If a woman is a queen, then she is the wife of a king (F)
   (she could be the eldest daughter of a king with no sons)
   Converse: If a woman is the wife of a king, then she is a queen (T)
   King
   Definition: a male sovereign
   Biconditional: A male is a king if and only if he is a sovereign
   Conditional: If a male is a king, then he is a sovereign (T)
   Converse: If a male is a sovereign, then he is a king (F)

GEOMETRY LAB 2-6
Design Plans for Proofs

Activity

6.

1. $\angle AXB \cong \angle CXD$ (Given)

2. $m\angle AXB = m\angle CXD$ (Def. of $\cong$ $\angle$s)

3. $m\angle BXC = m\angle BXC$ (Reflex. Prop. of $=$)

Holt McDougal Geometry

4. m∠AXB + m∠BXC = m∠CXD + mBXC (Add. Prop. of =)

5. m∠AXB + m∠BXC = m∠AXC, m∠BXC + m∠CXD = m∠BXD (∠ Add. Post.)

6. m∠AXC = m∠BXD (Subst.)

7. ∠AXC ≅ ∠BXD (Def. of ≅ ∠s)

Try This

1. Possible answer: A plan for a proof is less formal than a proof. A formal proof presents every logical step in detail, but a plan describes only the key logical steps.

2. Plan: Use the def. of ∠bis. to show that m∠1 = m∠2. Then use the ∠ Add. Post. and subst. to show that 2m∠1 = m∠ABC.

Two-column Proof:

1. $\overleftrightarrow{BD}$ bisects ∠ABC. (Given)

2. ∠1 ≅ ∠2 (Def. of ∠ bis.)

3. m∠1 = m∠2 (Def. of ≅ ∠s)

4. m∠1 + m∠2 = m∠ABC (∠ Add. Post.)

5. m∠1 + m∠1 = m∠ABC (Subst.)

6. 2m∠1 = m∠ABC (Simplify.)

3. Plan: Since ∠LXN is a right angle, its measure is 90°. By the ∠ Add. Post., m∠1 + m∠2 = m∠LXN. So by subst., m∠1 + m∠2 = 90°, which means that ∠1 and ∠2 are comp.

Two-column proof:

1. ∠LXN is a rt. ∠. (Given)

2. m∠LXN = 90° (Def of rt. ∠)

3. m∠1 + m∠2 = m∠LXN (∠ Add. Post.)

4. m∠1 + m∠2 = 90° (Subst.)

5. ∠1 and ∠2 are comp. (Def. of comp. ∠s)

TECHNOLOGY LAB 2-7
Proving the Vertical Angles Theorem

Activity

∠EAC = 67.02°

Try This

1. a. Check student's sketches

b. Answers will vary depending on the sketch.

c. They have the same measure.

d. Find the sum of the measures of the adjacent angles and show that each pair add to 180°.

Holt McDougal Geometry

CHAPTER 3 — Answers for Parallel and Perpendicular Lines

TECHNOLOGY LAB 3-2
Explore Parallel Lines and Transversals

Activity

4. Possible measures are given in the table.

Possible answer: All acute ∠s are ≅. All obtuse ∠s are ≅. Any acute ∠ is supp. to any obtuse ∠.

∠AGE	∠BGE	∠AGH	∠BGH	∠CHG	∠DHG	∠CHF	∠DHF
100°	80°	80°	100°	100°	80°	80°	100°
72°	108°	108°	72°	72°	108°	108°	72°

Try This

1. The corr. ∠s are the pairs ∠AGE and ∠CHG, ∠BGE and ∠DHG, ∠AGH and ∠CHF, and ∠BGH and ∠DHF. The ∠s in each pair have = measures.

2. The alt. int. ∠s are the pairs ∠CHG and ∠BGH, and ∠AGH and ∠DHG. The ∠s in each pair have = measures.

   The alt. ext. ∠s are the pairs ∠AGE and ∠DHF, and ∠BGE and ∠CHF. The ∠s in each pair have = measures.

   The same-side int. ∠s are the pairs ∠CHG and ∠AGH, and ∠BGH and ∠DHG. The angles in each pair have measures that add up to 180°.

3. Possible answer: If the ∥ lines are dragged farther apart or closer together, there is no change in the ∠ measures. Since the lines remain ∥, the amount of "tilt" of the line remains the same, so the ∠ measures remain the same.

GEOMETRY LAB 3-2
Investigating Angles Formed by Parallel Lines Cut by a Transversal

Activity

Step 1
m∠1 = 50°   m∠2 = 130°
m∠3 = 50°   m∠4 = 130°
m∠5 = 50°   m∠6 = 130°

m∠7 = 50°   m∠8 = 130°

Step 2
∠1 ≅ ∠3   ∠1 ≅ ∠5   ∠3 ≅ ∠5
∠2 ≅ ∠4   ∠2 ≅ ∠6   ∠4 ≅ ∠6
∠5 ≅ ∠7   ∠3 ≅ ∠7   ∠1 ≅ ∠7
∠6 ≅ ∠8   ∠4 ≅ ∠8   ∠2 ≅ ∠8

Step 3
a. ∠1 and ∠3   ∠2 and ∠4   ∠5 and ∠7
   ∠6 and ∠8
b. ∠1 and ∠5   ∠2 and ∠6   ∠4 and ∠8
   ∠3 and ∠7
c. ∠1 and ∠7   ∠2 and ∠8
d. ∠3 and ∠5   ∠4 and ∠6

Try This

1. are congruent
2. are congruent
3. are congruent
4. are congruent

GEOMETRY LAB 3-3
Construct Parallel Lines

Try This

1. Yes; the lines are still ∥.
2. Check students' work.
3. ∥ Post.
4. If you draw quadrilateral PQRS in the diagram, then it is a rhombus, because the same compass setting was used to construct all 4 side lengths.
5. Yes; the lines are still ∥.
6. The corr. ∠s measure 90°. By the Conv. of the Corr. ∠s Post, the lines must be ∥.
7. Check students' work.
8. The lines are ∥.

Holt McDougal Geometry

GEOMETRY LAB 3-4
Construct Perpendicular Lines

1. Check students' work.

2. Check students' work.

3. Check students' work. The lines are ∥ because two lines that are ⊥ to the same line are ∥ to each other.

GEOMETRY LAB 3-4
Angles Formed by Perpendicular Lines

Line	1	2	3	4	5	6	7	8
Slope	1	−1	$\frac{1}{4}$	−4	$\frac{2}{3}$	$-\frac{3}{2}$	0	∞

1. −1

2. −1

3. −1

4. They are negative reciprocals of each other

5. They form four 90° angles or they intersect at right angles

6. $-\frac{8}{3}$

7. right angle or 90° angle; negative reciprocals

8. they are perpendicular because they intersect at right angles, also ∞ is kind of like $\frac{1}{0}$ so they are sort of reciprocals and 0 has not sign so the negative part does not matter

GEOMETRY LAB 3-5
Investigating Lines in the Coordinate Plane

Line	1	2	3	4
Slope	$\frac{1}{2}$	$\frac{1}{2}$	$\frac{1}{2}$	$\frac{1}{2}$
y-intercept	4	2.5	0	−4
Position	Far above	Above	At	Far below
Steepness/ Direction	gentle, rising	gentle, rising	gentle, rising	gentle, rising

1. The y-intercept determines the position of the line, a positive y-intercept is above the origin and a negative y-intercept is below the origin; the larger the intercept's absolute value, the further away from the origin the line is

2. It would be really far above the origin.

Line	1	2	3	4	5	6
Slope	2.5	0.5	0.1	−2	−0.75	−0.25
y-intercept	2.5	2.5	2.5	−2	−2	−2
Position	Above	Above	Above	Below	Below	Below
Steepness/ Direction	steep, rising	gentle, rising	gentle, rising	steep, falling	moderate, falling	gentle, falling

3. The greater the absolute value of the slope, the steeper the line is, slopes with absolute value between 0 and 1 are flatter. A positive slope rises and a negative slope falls (left to right).

4. It would be extremely steep and falling down

5. Steepness and direction; position

TECHNOLOGY LAB 3-6A
Explore Parallel and Perpendicular Lines

Activity 1

1. $y = 3x - 4$ and $y = 3x + 1$ appear to be ∥. The slopes of the lines are the same.

2. Possible answer: $y = 2x + 1$; the slope of the new line is 2.

3. Possible answer: $y = -\frac{1}{2}x + 1$; the slope of the new line is $-\frac{1}{2}$.

Try This

1. Possible answer: $y = x$ and $y = x + 1$; the lines are still ∥ if the window setting is changed.

2. Possible answers: Yes; both lines appear steeper.

3. Changing the y-intercept of the lines does not change whether they are ∥.

Activity 2

1. yes

2. Possible answer: $y = -\frac{1}{3}x + 1$; the slope of the new line is $-\frac{1}{3}$.

3. Possible answer: $y = -\frac{3}{2}x$; the slope of the new line is $-\frac{3}{2}$.

Try This

4. The student's equations should have slopes that are opp. reciprocals of each other. The product of the 2 slopes should be −1.

5. Possible answers: No; the lines still intersect, but the angle does not look like a right angle.

6. Changing the y-intercept of the lines does not change whether they are ⊥.

TECHNOLOGY LAB 3-6B
Walk the Line: Straight Line Distance Graphs

Sample Results
Actual data will vary.

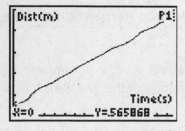

Raw data in DATAMATE

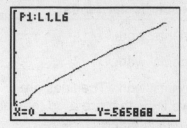

Data re-graphed
with trace to y-intercept

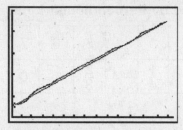

Optimized model fit

Calculator regression result

Data Table
Sample data; actual data may vary.

y-intercept b	0.565 m
optimized slope m	0.25 m/s
optimized line equation	$y = 0.565 + 0.25*x$
(x_1, y_1)	0, 0.565
(x_2, y_2)	1.6, 1.01
regression line equation	$y = 0.25*x + 0.62$

Holt McDougal Geometry

Try This

1. The slope determined by the two-point calculation is nearly the same as the one found by trial and error.

2. The slope and intercept determined by the calculator are similar to those obtained by trial and error. They are not exactly the same, but you would not expect them to be the same. The trial and error line used only one point to determine the *y*-intercept, while the calculator used all the points.

3. Slope represents a change in distance from the motion detector divided by a change in time.

4. The slope has units of meters per second, or m/s.

5. The slope represents the velocity of the walker.

TECHNOLOGY LAB 3-6C
Graphing Your Motion

1. The second graph is steeper.

2. Distance vs. Time

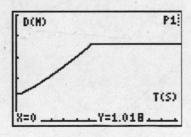

Matching Distance vs. Time

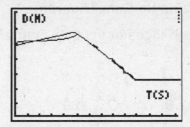

The slope of the portion of the graph corresponding to movement is greater for the faster trial.

Results will probably vary between groups as they may walk at different rates.

Walking towards the motion detector will produce a negative slope. While walking away from the motion detector will produce a positive slope.

Holt McDougal Geometry

GEOMETRY LAB 4-2
Develop the Triangle Sum Theorem

1. When placed together the 3 ∠s form a line.

2. yes

3. m∠A + m∠B + m∠C = 180°

4. The sum of the measures of the ∠s of a △ is 180°.

TECHNOLOGY LAB 4-2
Angle Relationships in Triangles

1. acute; 83.32°, 35.02°, 61.66°

2. right; 90°, 49.09°, 40.91°

3. obtuse; 109.32°, 21.58°, 49.11°

GEOMETRY LAB 4-4
Explore SSS and SAS Triangle Congruence

1. yes

2. It is not possible. Once the lengths of the 3 straws are determined, only 1 △ can be formed.

3. To prove that 2 △s are ≅, check to see if the 3 pairs of corr. sides are ≅.

4. three sides of 1 △ are ≅ to 3 sides of the other △

5. yes

6. No; once 2 side lengths and the included ∠ measure are determined, only 1 length is possible for the remaining side.

7. To prove that 2 △s are ≅, check to see if there are 2 pairs of ≅ corr. sides and that their included ∠s are ≅.

8. Check students' work.

9. 2 sides and the included ∠ of 1 △ are ≅ to 2 sides and the included ∠ of the other △.

GEOMETRY LAB 4-4
Investigating Triangle Congruence: SSS and SAS

1.

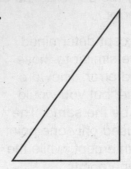

2.

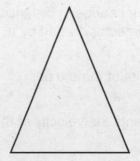

3.

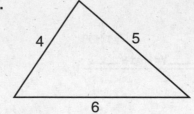

4.

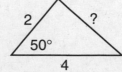

5.

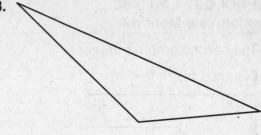

Holt McDougal Geometry

TECHNOLOGY LAB 4-5
Predict Other Triangle Congruence Relationships

Activity 1

1. Check students' constructions.

2. Check students' constructions.

3. It stays the same.

4. Check students' constructions.

Try This

1. Yes; the △ stays the same shape if you do not change *AD* or the measures of ∠*A* and ∠*D*.

2. No

3. Third ∠s Thm.

4. No; the ∠ measures may stay the same, but the side lengths can vary.

5. Check students' constructions; yes; yes; AAS.

6. You need the length of 1 side of the △. In an AAS combination, if 2 corr. ∠s and sides are ≅, then only 1 △ is made.

Activity 2

7. Many; no

8. 1

9. rt.

10. rt. ∠s

TECHNOLOGY LAB 5-1A
Developing and Using the Triangle Midsegment Theorem

1. 31.5 units; 63 units

2. 19.5 units; 39 units

3. 5 units; 10 units

TECHNOLOGY LAB 5-1B
Perpendicular and Angle Bisector

1.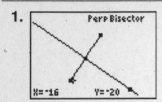

2.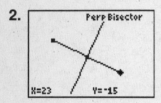

3.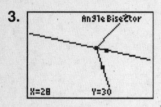

4.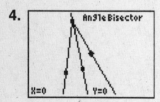

TECHNOLOGY LAB 5-2
Bisectors of Triangles

1.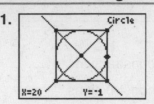

2.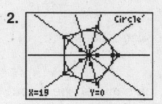

3.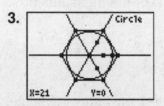

TECHNOLOGY LAB 5-3
Special Points in Triangles

1. the circumcenter, the orthocenter, and the centroid

2. The centroid; possible answer: the distance from the centroid to the orthocenter is twice the distance from the centroid to the circumcenter; that is, $CO = 2CU$.

3. isosceles triangle

4. equilateral triangle

Holt McDougal Geometry

GEOMETRY LAB 5-3
Bisectors of Triangles

Check students posters.

GEOMETRY LAB 5-5
Explore Triangle Inequalities

1. Check students' work.

2. Possible answer: The longest side is opp. the largest $\angle$, and the shortest side is opp. the smallest $\angle$.

3. Check students' work.

4. only the set with lengths 3 in., 4 in., and 6 in.

5. Possible answer: If the sum of any 2 lengths is greater than the third length, then the set of stems can form a $\triangle$. If the sum of any 2 lengths is equal to or less than the third length, then the set of stems cannot form a $\triangle$.

6. Check students' work.

GEOMETRY LAB 5-7
Hands-On Proof of the Pythagorean Theorem

4. a; a^2; b; b^2

5. $a^2 + b^2$

6.

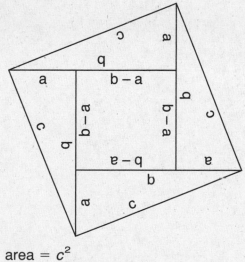

area = c^2

Try This

1. $a^2 + b^2 = c^2$

2. Check students' work.

TECHNOLOGY LAB 5-7
Pythagorean Theorem

1. It is a right triangle.

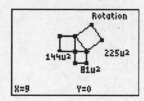

2. It is a right triangle.

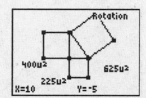

3. It is not a right triangle.

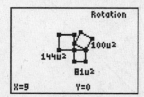

GEOMETRY LAB 5-8
Graph Irrational Numbers

1.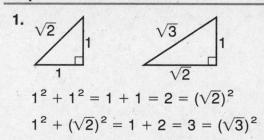

$1^2 + 1^2 = 1 + 1 = 2 = (\sqrt{2})^2$

$1^2 + (\sqrt{2})^2 = 1 + 2 = 3 = (\sqrt{3})^2$

2. Check students' constructions to confirm that $\sqrt{4}$ lies at 2 on the number line.

3. Check students' constructions to confirm that $\sqrt{9}$ lies at 3 on the number line.

Holt McDougal Geometry

4. Check students' constructions to confirm that $2\sqrt{2}$ lies at $\sqrt{8}$ on the number line.

GEOMETRY LAB 5-8
Reflecting Special Right Triangles

1.

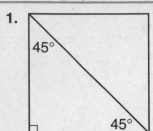

2.

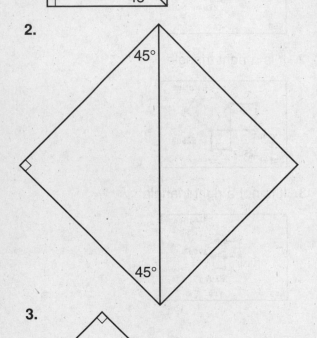

3.

4.

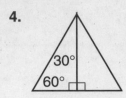

5.

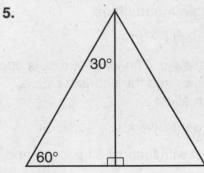

6.

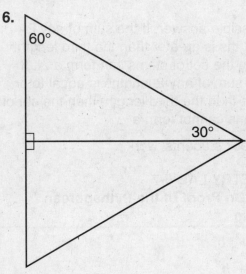

GEOMETRY LAB 6-1
Construct Regular Polygons

1. Possible answer: Draw a line ℓ. Draw *A* and *D* on ℓ. Construct *m* ⊥ to ℓ through *A*. Construct *n* ⊥ to ℓ through *D*. Set the compass to the length *AD*. With the compass point at *A*, draw an arc that intersects *m* above ℓ. Label the pt. of intersection *B*. With the compass point at *D*, draw an arc that intersects *n* above ℓ. Label the pt. of intersection *C*. Draw $\overline{BC}$. The polygon *ABCD* is a reg. quad.

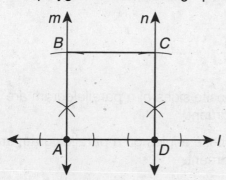

2. The circle is circumscribed about the polygon.

3. Check students' work. Possible answer:

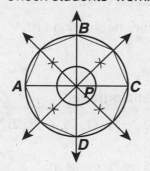

4. Possible answer: The 6 sides of *ABCDEF* were marked off with the same compass setting, so they are ≅. When $\overline{AD}$, $\overline{BE}$, and $\overline{CF}$ are drawn, the 6 △s formed are ≅ and equil. The measure of each ∠ of an equil. △ is 60°. Each ∠ of the hexagon is formed by 2 of these

60° ∠s, so the 6 ∠s of *ABCDEF* are ≅. Since it has 6 ≅ sides and 6 ≅ ∠s, *ABCDEF* is a reg. hexagon.

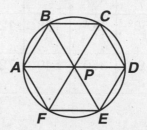

5. Check students' work. Possible answer: Draw $\overline{AD}$, $\overline{BE}$, and $\overline{CF}$. Construct the bisectors of ∠*APB*, ∠*BPC*, ∠*CPD*, ∠*DPE*, ∠*EPF*, and ∠*FPA*. Connect the 6 pts. where the ∠ bisectors intersect the circle to pts. *A*, *B*, *C*, *D*, *E*, and *F* in order around the circle.

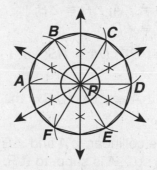

6. Check students' work. Possible answer: Bisect ∠*EPF*, ∠*FPG*, ∠*GPH*, ∠*HPJ*, and ∠*JPE*. Connect the 5 pts. where the ∠ bisectors intersect the circle to pts. *E*, *F*, *G*, *H*, and *J* in order around the circle.

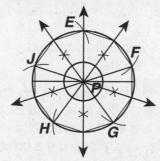

Holt McDougal Geometry

7.

Regular Polygons				
Number of Sides	3	4	5	6
Measure of Each Angle	60°	90°	108°	120°
Sum of Angle Measures	180°	360°	540°	720°

8. $(n - 2)180°$

9. $\dfrac{(n - 2)180°}{n}$

GEOMETRY LAB 6-2
Explore Properties of Parallelogram

1. Check students' work.

2. $\overline{QR} \cong \overline{AB}$; $\overline{RS} \cong \overline{BC}$; $\overline{ST} \cong \overline{CD}$; $\overline{TQ} \cong \overline{DA}$; $\angle Q \cong \angle A$; $\angle R \cong \angle B$; $\angle S \cong \angle C$; $\angle T \cong \angle D$

3. $AB = ST$; $\overline{AB} \cong \overline{CD}$; $DA = RS$; $\overline{DA} \cong \overline{BC}$

4. $m\angle A = m\angle S$; $\angle A \cong \angle C$; $m\angle B = m\angle T$; $\angle B \cong \angle D$

5. $\overline{QR}$ and $\overline{AB}$ are collinear. $\angle A$ and $\angle R$ form a lin. pair, so $\angle A$ is supp. to $\angle R$. Since $\angle R \cong \angle B$, $\angle A$ is supp. to $\angle B$.

6. The creases intersect at the same pt. where $\overline{AC}$ and $\overline{BD}$ intersect. So the diags. intersect at the mdpt. of each, and therefore the diags. bisect each other.

Try This

1. Check students' work. They should obtain the same results.

2. Possible answers: If a quad. is a ▱, then its opp. sides are ≅. If a quad. is a ▱, then its opp. ∠s are ≅. If a quad. is a ▱, then its cons. ∠s are supp. If a quad. is a ▱, then its diags. intersect at their mdpts.

TECHNOLOGY LAB 6-3
Investigating Properties of Parallelograms

Lab 6-2
Activity
Step 2
The side lengths of opposite sides are the same.
The angles measures of opposite angles are the same measure.
The measures add up to 360°.
Step 3
No
No

Try This

1. No

2. Opposite sides of a parallelogram are congruent.

3. Opposite angles on a parallelogram are congruent.

4. The sum of the angle measures in a parallelogram is 360°.

5. Check student's constructions; all properties should be valid.

6. Properties will vary depending on students figure.

GEOMETRY LAB 6-3
Conditions for Parallelograms

1. **a.** $(-5, -1)$, $(-1, -1)$, $(1, 2)$, $(-3, 2)$
   b. parallelogram

2. **a.** $(1, 3)$, $(-1, 1)$, $(2, -2)$, $(4, 0)$
   b. parallelogram

3. **a.** $(1, 4)$, $(1, 2)$, $(-2, -1)$, $(-2, 1)$
   b. parallelogram

4. **a.** $(3, 2)$, $(0, 1)$, $(-3, -1)$, $(0, 2)$
   b. parallelogram

5. **a.** $(-2, -3)$, $(3, -3)$, $(5, -1)$, $(0, -1)$
   b. parallelogram

Holt McDougal Geometry

6. The figure connecting the midpoints of the four sides any quadrilateral will always form a parallelogram.

7. Parallelogram

GEOMETRY LAB 6-4
Using Tangrams to Study Properties of Rectangles, Rhombuses and Squares

1.

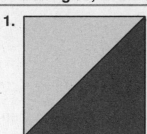

Area = 8

Area = 2

2.

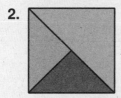

Area = 4

3.

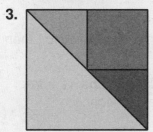

Area = 8

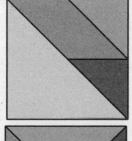

Area = 8

4.

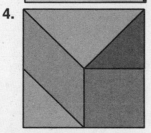

Area = 8

5. Not possible because the combinations of six pieces add up to 12, 14, or 15, so the sides would have lengths: $2\sqrt{3}$, $\sqrt{14}$, or $\sqrt{15}$; none of the pieces have these sizes so you can not create a square!

6.

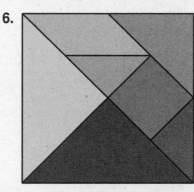

Area = 16

7.

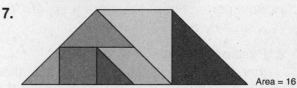

Area = 16

8.

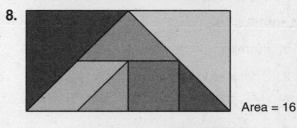

Area = 16

9.

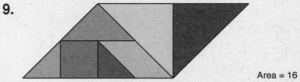

Area = 16

10.

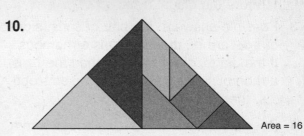

Area = 16

Holt McDougal Geometry

TECHNOLOGY LAB 6-5
Predict Conditions for Special Parallelograms

Activity 1

1. Check students' work.

2. Check students' work.

3. Check students' work.

4. rectangle

5. Check students' work.

6. rectangle

Try This

1. Both pairs of opp. sides are ∥, so *ABCD* is a ▱ by def.

2. Possible answers: If a ▱ has a rt. ∠, then it is a rect. If a ▱ has ≅ diags., then it is a rect.

Activity 2

1. rhombus

2. Check students' work.

3. Check students' work.

4. rhombus

5. Check students' work.

6. rhombus

Try This

3. Possible answers: If a pair of cons. sides of a ▱ are ≅, then the ▱ is a rhombus. If the diags. of a ▱ are ⊥, then the ▱ is a rhombus. If a diag. of a ▱ bisects opp. ∠s, then the ▱ is a rhombus.

4. Possible answers: If a ▱ is a rect. and a rhombus, then the ▱ is a square.

TECHNOLOGY LAB 6-6
Explore Isosceles Trapezoids

Activity 1

1. Check students' work.

2. Check students' work.

3. Check students' work.

4. m∠*CAB* = m∠*ABD*; m∠*ACD* = m∠*CDB*

5. *AC* = *BD*

Try This

1. Possible answer: If a trap. is isosc., then its base ∠s are ≅.

2. Possible answer: If 1 pair of base ∠s of a trap. are ≅, then the trap. is isosc.

Activity 2

1. Check students' work.

2. Check students' work.

3. *AD* = *CB*

4. *AC* = *BD*

Try This

3. Possible answer: If a trap. is isosc., then its diags. are ≅.

4. Possible answer: If the diags. of a trap. are ≅, then the trap. is isosc.

GEOMETRY LAB 6-6
Using a Geoboard to Study Properties of Kites and Trapezoids

Activity – Trapezoid

1. III

2. parallel

3. (−3, 4), (4, 4), (4, −2) and (−3, −2)

4. $6 \cdot 7 = 42$

5. 42

6. 7

7. $4 + 10 = 14$

8. average; median; height (in any order)

Activity – Kite

1. non-vertex; equal

2. perpendicular

3. perpendicular bisector

4. diagonal; bisects

5. symmetry

TECHNOLOGY LAB 6-6
Developing and Using the Trapezoid Midsegment Theorem

1. 25 units; 10 units and 40 units

2. 30 units; 20 units and 40 units

3. 21.5 units; 12 units and 31 units

Holt McDougal Geometry

CHAPTER 7 — Answers for Similarity

TECHNOLOGY LAB 7-2
Explore the Golden Ratio

Activity 1

1. Check students' work. The equal ratios have the approximate value of 1.62.

4. The ratios have the same value as the ratios in step 1.

Try This

1. If the side length of the square is 2 units, then $MB = 1$ unit, and $BC = 2$ units. $\overline{MC}$ is the hyp. of the rt. $\triangle$ formed by $\overline{MB}$ and $\overline{BC}$. By the Pyth. Thm., $\overline{MC}$ has length $\sqrt{5}$ units. $\overline{AE}$ has length $\sqrt{5} + 1$ units. The ratio of $\overline{AE}$ to $\overline{EF}$ is $\frac{\sqrt{5} + 1}{2}$, or about 1.618.

2. $\overline{BE}$ has length $\sqrt{5} - 1$ units. The ratio of $\overline{BE}$ to $\overline{EF}$ is $\frac{\sqrt{5} - 1}{2}$, or about 0.618. The sign of the numerator in this fraction is different from that of the fraction in Try This **Problem 1**.

3. The quotients have values that approach 1.618.

4. There are $1 + 1 = 2$ rabbits.

5. There are $8 + 13 = 21$ petals on the daisy.

6. no; $\frac{5.4}{4} \approx 1.4$

7. yes; $\frac{4.5}{2.8} \approx 1.6$

GEOMETRY LAB 7-2
Investigating Ratios in Similar Polygons

Activity

1. Sides are proportional and angles are congruent

2. 2 or $\frac{1}{2}$

3. 10 and $5\sqrt{5}$

Try This

1. a. Sides are proportional and angles are congruent
   b. 2 or $\frac{1}{2}$
   c. $4\sqrt{5}$

2. a. Sides are proportional and angles are congruent
   b. 2 or $\frac{1}{2}$
   c. 9, $3\sqrt{5}$, $3\sqrt{10}$

3. a. Sides are proportional and angles are congruent
   b. 2 or $\frac{1}{2}$
   c. $5\sqrt{5}$, $10\sqrt{2}$, $5\sqrt{5}$, $10\sqrt{2}$

4. Both could be correct; it depends which figure you label as the first figure. If the problem labeled one as the first figure then you must give the scale factor in that order.

TECHNOLOGY LAB 7-3
Predict Triangle Similar Relationships

Activity 1

3. The ratios of corr. side lengths are =.

Try This

1. $\triangle$ Sum Thm.

2. Yes; in $\sim$ $\triangle$s, corr. sides are proportional.

Activity 2

3. Corr. $\angle$s are $\cong$.

Try This

3. Yes; if 2 $\triangle$s have their corr. sides in the same ratio, then the $\triangle$s are $\sim$.

4. They are similar in that both allow you to conclude that corr. $\angle$s are $\cong$. They are different in that the conjecture suggests that $\triangle$s with corr. sides in the same ratio have the same shape, but the SSS $\cong$ Thm. allows you to conclude that the $\triangle$s have both the same shape and the same size.

Activity 3

3. The ratio of the corr. sides of △*ABC* and △*DEF* are proportional.

4. The corr. ∠s of the △s are ≅.

Try This

5. Yes; corr. sides are proportional and corr. ∠s are ≅.

6. If △s have 2 pairs of corr. sides in proportion and the included ∠s are ≅, then the △s are ∼. This is related to the SAS ≅ Thm.

TECHNOLOGY LAB 7-4
Investigate Angle Bisector of a Triangle

Activity 1

2. $\dfrac{BD}{AB} = \dfrac{CD}{AC}$ or $\dfrac{BD}{CD} = \dfrac{AB}{AC}$

Try These

1. Check students' work; the segments created by an ∠ bisector will be in proportion to the adj. sides.

2. $\dfrac{BD}{CD} = \dfrac{AB}{AC}$ or $\dfrac{BD}{AB} = \dfrac{CD}{AC}$

Activity 2

2. Check students' work.

3. $\dfrac{DI}{DG} = \dfrac{DE + DF}{\text{perimenter } \triangle DEF}$

4. $\dfrac{DI}{DG} = \dfrac{DE + DF}{DE + DF + EF}$; the length of the segment from the vertex of the bisected ∠ to the incenter divided by the length of the segment from the vertex to the opposite side is = to the sum of the sides of the bisected ∠ divided by the perimeter of the △.

Try These

3. Check students' work.

4. Check students' work.

GEOMETRY LAB 7-6
Studying Similarity in the Coordinate Plane

1. **a.** Acute triangle or general triangle
   b. Answers will vary: (1, 0), (4, 0), (2, −4)

2. **a.** Obtuse triangle
   b. Answers will vary: (0, −1), (2, −3), (5, 3)

3. **a.** Parallelogram
   b. Answers will vary: (−1, 0), (5, 0), (3, −4), (−3, −4)

4. **a.** Trapezoid
   b. Answers will vary: (1, 0), (3, −2), (−1, 0), (−2, −2)

5. **a.** Quadrilateral
   b. Answers will vary: (−2, 5), (4, 5), (4, −4) and (5, −1)

6. **a.** Pentagon
   b. Answers will vary: (0, −1), (2, −3), (1, −5), (−1, −5), (−2, −3)

7. The square has equal perpendicular sides so the sides align with the two axes. The rhombus has equal slanted sides, so one pair will align with one of the axes but the other will not and the pegs will not measure the correct length for the other pair of sides.

8. All circles are similar to one another, so there is no advantage to drawing a similar circle.

Holt McDougal Geometry

GEOMETRY LAB 8-1
Brightness of Light

2.

Distance	Intensity
0.10	348
0.15	151
0.20	85
0.25	55
0.30	39
0.50	18
0.75	11
1.00	10

Background Answers will vary.

TECHNOLOGY LAB 8-2
Explore Trigonometric Ratios

1. m∠A stays the same. Each △ will have 2 ∠s (∠DEA and ∠A) ≅ to 2 ∠s in every other △, so by the AA Similarity Post., these △s are similar to each other

2. The values of the ratios do not change, because the ratios of the side lengths are equal in similar △s.

3. As C moves, m∠A changes. Once C is in a new position, moving D does not change the ratios.

4. $\frac{DE}{AE} = 1$, and m∠A = 45°. If $\frac{DE}{AD} = \frac{AE}{AD}$, then DE = AE, so $\frac{DE}{AE} = 1$. Since 2 sides are equal, △DEA is an isosc. △. It is also a rt. △. Thus △DEA must be a 45°-45°-90° special rt. △, so m∠A = 45°.

TECHNOLOGY LAB 8-2
Trigonometric Ratios

1.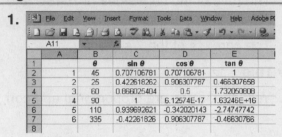

2. =1/SIN(RADIANS(B2))

GEOMETRY LAB 8-4
Indirect Measurement Using Trigonometry

1. The ∠ reading from the clinometer is the comp. of the ∠ of elevation.

2. Check students' work.

3. Check students' work. The results should be similar.

4. Possible answers: measuring the distance between the observer and the object, measuring the height of the eyes of the observer, and reading the ∠ measure from the clinometer.

5. It can be used to measure the height of tall objects that cannot be measured directly.

Holt McDougal Geometry

GEOMETRY LAB 9-1
Investigating Reflections Over the
Line y = x

Activity

6. $y = -2x + 8$

8. $y = x$

Try This

6. $y = x - 3$

7. $y = -x - 1$

8. $y = \frac{1}{2}x + 1$

TECHNOLOGY LAB 9-3
Use a Graphing Calculator to Explore
Transformations

Activity 1

1.

$[B] = \begin{bmatrix} 1 & 2 & 5 \\ 0 & 4 & 3 \end{bmatrix}$

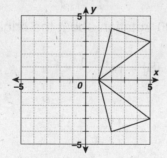

2. ([A] ↓ [B] shown on page in calc screen)

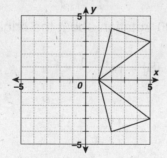

a reflection across the *x*-axis

Try This

1. [A] [B] = $\begin{bmatrix} -1 & -2 & -5 \\ 0 & 4 & 3 \end{bmatrix}$

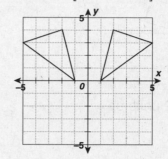

a reflection across the *y*-axis

2. [A] [B] = $\begin{bmatrix} 0 & 4 & 3 \\ 1 & 2 & 5 \end{bmatrix}$

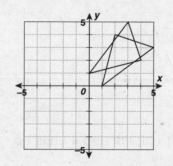

a reflection across the line $y = x$

Activity 2

1.

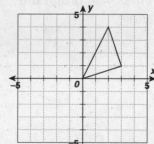

$[B] = \begin{bmatrix} 0 & 3 & 2 \\ 0 & 1 & 4 \end{bmatrix}$

Holt McDougal Geometry

2. ([A] ↓ [B] shown on page in calc screen)

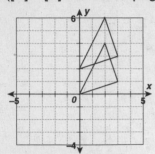

a translation 2 units up

Try This

3. $[A] + [B] = \begin{bmatrix} -1 & 2 & 1 \\ 4 & 5 & 8 \end{bmatrix}$

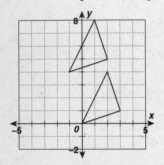

a translation 1 unit left and 4 units up

4. Let $[A] = \begin{bmatrix} a & a & a \\ b & b & b \end{bmatrix}$. Add [A] + [B] and use the solution matrix to graph the image of the triangle.

Activity 3

1.

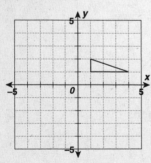

$[B] = \begin{bmatrix} 1 & 4 & 1 \\ 1 & 1 & 2 \end{bmatrix}$

2. $[A] \downarrow [B] = \begin{bmatrix} -1 & -1 & -2 \\ 1 & 4 & 1 \end{bmatrix}$

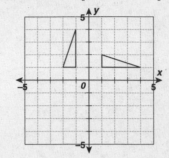

a 90° rotation about the origin

Try This

5. $[A] \downarrow [B] = \begin{bmatrix} -1 & -4 & -1 \\ -1 & -1 & -2 \end{bmatrix}$

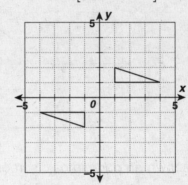

a 180° rotation about the origin

6. $[A] \downarrow [B] = \begin{bmatrix} 1 & 1 & 2 \\ -1 & -4 & -1 \end{bmatrix}$

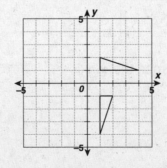

a 270° rotation about the origin

Holt McDougal Geometry

GEOMETRY LAB 9-6
Transformations to Extend Tessellations

1. Check students' work.

2. Check students' work.

3. Check students' work.

4. Check students' work.

5. Possible answer: this tessellation has rotation symmetry and translation symmetry, but the one created in Activity 1 has only translation symmetry.

6. Check students' work.

TECHNOLOGY LAB 9-6
Creating Tessellations

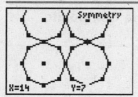

Holt McDougal Geometry

GEOMETRY LAB 10-2
Develop π

Activity 1

Try This

1. No; possible answer: all circles are similar, so the ratio of circumference to diameter is always the same.

2. Solving the relationship for *C* gives a formula in terms of *d* and π.

3. If the circumference is *n*π, then the diameter is *n*. Check students' measurements.

Activity 2

1-3. Check students' constructions.

4. Check students' measurements.

5. because π is the ratio of the circumference to the diameter; possible answer: 2.8 < π < 4

Try This

1. 3 < π < 3.46

2. Possible answer: The second inequality values are closer together. With more sides, the values would be even closer together. You can estimate π by averaging the upper and lower values.

3. Possible answer: Average the areas of the inscribed and circumscribed polygons.

TECHNOLOGY LAB 10-2
Developing Formulas for Circles and Regular Polygons

Circle	Radius	Radius²	Area	Area / Radius²
1	Sample Answer: 8	Sample Answer: 64	Sample Answer: 201.06	3.14
2	Sample Answer: 11	Sample Answer: 121	Sample Answer: 380.13	3.14
3	Sample Answer: 20	Sample Answer: 400	Sample Answer: 1256.64	3.14

4. $A \approx 3.14r^2$

GEOMETRY LAB 10-3
Using Tangrams to Create Composite Figures

1.
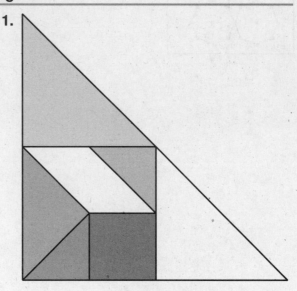

2.
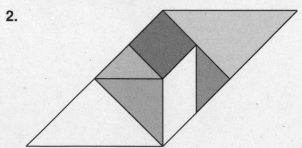

Holt McDougal Geometry

3.

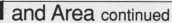

GEOMETRY LAB 10-3
Develop Pick's Formula

Activity 1

1-3.

Figure	Area	Number of Lattice Points	
		On Boundary	In Interior
A	2.5	5	1
B	2.5	5	1
C	3.5	5	2
D	4.5	5	3
E	5.5	5	4
F	5.5	5	4
G	3	6	1
H	3	6	1
I	4	6	2
J	4	6	2
K	5	6	3
L	6	6	4
M	3.5	7	1
N	3.5	7	1
O	4.5	7	2
P	5.5	7	3
Q	5.5	7	3
R	6.5	7	4

Try This

1. Possible answer: $A = \frac{1}{2}B + I - 1$

2. Check students' work.

3. Possible answer: 5 units^2

4. 6.5 units^2; no

TECHNOLOGY LAB 10-5
Effects of Changing Dimensions Proportionally

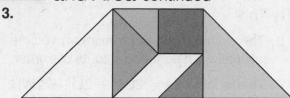

	A	B	C	D
1	Rectangle	Length	Width	Perimeter
2	A	8	4	24
3	B	4	2	12
4				
5	Ratios	2	2	2
6				

1. 2 : 1

2. 2 : 1

3. reduced by $\frac{1}{4}$ is reduced by $\frac{1}{2}$.

GEOMETRY LAB 10-6
Use Geometry Probability to Estimate π

1. Check students' work.

2. a. πr^2

  b. $4r^2$

  c. $\frac{\pi r^2}{4r^2} = \frac{\pi}{4}$

3. The probability is $\frac{\pi}{4}$, so 4 times the probability is π.

Holt McDougal Geometry

TECHNOLOGY LAB 11-4
Compare Surface Areas and Volumes

Activity 1

4. Check students' work. The rectangular prism with the minimum surface area for a given volume is a cube. Students may not have an exact cube in their spreadsheet, but their smallest surface area will be the surface area of the prism that is most cubical.

Try This

1. The cylinder with the minimum surface area will be the one in which the height and the diameter are closest to each other.

2. Possible answer: No; a package such as a cereal box might be designed to have a large surface area so that it stands out more on the shelf.

Activity 2

2. The rectangular prism with the maximum volume for a given surface area is a cube. Students may not have an exact cube in their spreadsheet, but their greatest volume will be the volume of the prism that is most cubical.

Try This

3. The cylinder with the maximum volume will have a height equal to its diameter.

4. The formula SA = 2LW + 2LH + 2WH becomes $H = \dfrac{\left(\frac{SA}{2} - LW\right)}{(L + W)}$ when solved for H.

5. A sphere will have the minimum surface area and a pyramid will have the maximum surface area for a given volume.

6. If the dimensions of a rectangular prism are doubled, surface area is multiplied by 4 and the volume is multiplied by 8. So the ratio of surface area to volume is multiplied by $\frac{4}{8} = \frac{1}{2}$. Set up a spreadsheet as in Activity 1. Enter values for L, W, and H in one row, and enter the values 2L, 2W, and 2H in the next row. Repeat for several values of L, W, and H.

Holt McDougal Geometry

TECHNOLOGY LAB 12-2
Data Collection: Beverage Tests

Data Collection

1.-2. Check student's answers.

Try This

1.-10. Check student's answers.

11. Students will classify acidic beverages with vinegar (pH $<$ 7), basic beverages (pH $>$ 7) with ammonia, and neutral liquids (pH $=$ 7) with water. Some students may use pH to describe most beverages as being a weaker acid or base compared to vinegar and ammonia.

GEOMETRY LAB 12-3
Use Sectors to Find the Area of a Circle Length

Activity

3. parallelogram

4. yes

5. parallelogram; the approximation becomes closer

Try This

1. The base of the assembled figure is approximately equal to half of the circumference because the base has the curved parts of the 4 out of 8 sectors which is half the circumference. Base $= \pi \cdot r$

2. Area $= \pi \cdot r \cdot r = \pi r^2$

3. The method becomes more realistic because as the number of sectors increases, the curved parts of the sectors become straighter.

TECHNOLOGY LAB 12-5
Explore Angle Relationships in Circles

Activity 1

5. Check students' tables. The measure of an $\angle$ formed by a tangent and a secant intersecting at the pt. of tangency will be half the measure of the intercepted arc.

Activity 2

5. Check students' tables. The measure of an $\angle$ formed by 2 secants (or chords) intersecting inside the $\odot$ will be half the sum of the measures of the intercepted arcs.

Activity 3

3. Check students' tables. The measure of an $\angle$ formed by 2 secants intersecting outside the $\odot$ will be half the difference of the measures of the intercepted arcs.

Try This

1. The relationship is the same. Both types of $\angle$s have a measure $=$ to half the measure of the arc.

2. A tangent line must be $\perp$ to the radius at the pt. of tangency. If the construction is done without this $\perp$ relationship, then the tangent line created is not guaranteed to intersect the $\odot$ at only 1 pt. If a line is $\perp$ to a radius of a $\odot$ at a pt. on the $\odot$, then the line is tangent to the $\odot$.

3. The relationship remains the same. The measure of the $\angle$ is half the difference of the intercepted arcs.

4. • an $\angle$ whose vertex is *on* the $\odot$ will have a measure $=$ to half its intercepted arc.

• an $\angle$ whose vertex is *inside* the $\odot$ will have a measure $=$ to half the sum of its intercepted arcs.

• an $\angle$ whose vertex is *outside* the $\odot$ will have a measure $=$ to half the difference of its intercepted arcs.

5. No; it is a means to discover relationships and make conjectures.

GEOMETRY LAB 12-5
Investigating Angle Relationships in Circles

Activity

5. It is $\frac{1}{2}$ the measure.

Holt McDougal Geometry

Try This

1. 25°

2. 150°

3. 90°

TECHNOLOGY LAB 12-6
Explore Segment Relationships in Circles

3. Check students' tables. The product of the lengths of the whole secant seg. and the ext. secant seg. will be = to the product of the other whole secant seg. and the other ext. secant seg.

Try This

1.

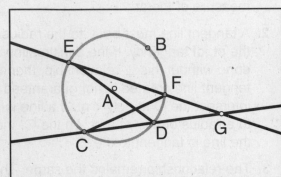

2. ∠CGF and ∠EGD; ∠FCG and ∠DEG; △CFG and △EDG are ~ △s by the AA ~ Post.

3. $\dfrac{GC}{GF} = \dfrac{GE}{GD}$; $GC \cdot GD = GE \cdot GF$

Activity 2

4. Check students' tables. The product of the lengths of segs. on a secant will be = to the square of the length of the tangent seg. from the same ext. pt.

Try This

4. The products of seg. lengths for a tangent and a secant are ~ to the products of seg. lengths for 2 secants because for a tangent there is only 1 seg. Thus the "whole segment" multiplied by the "ext. seg." becomes the square of the tangent seg.

5. Two tangent segs. from the same ext. pt. will have = lengths, so the segs. are ≅.

6. In the diagram, ⊙A is given with tangents $\overline{DC}$ and $\overline{DE}$ from D. Since 2 pts. determine a line, draw radii $\overline{AC}$, $\overline{AE}$, and $\overline{AD}$. $\overline{AC} \cong \overline{AE}$ because all radii are ≅. $\overline{AD} \cong \overline{AD}$ by the Reflex Prop. of ≅. ∠ACD and ∠AED are rt. ∠s because they are each formed by a radius and a tangent intersecting at the pt. of tangency. Thus △ACD and △AED are rt. △s. △ACD ≅ △AED by the HL ≅ Thm. Therefore $\overline{DC} \cong \overline{DE}$ by CPCTC.

Activity 3

3. Check students' tables. The product of the lengths of the segs. on 1 chord will = the product of the lengths of the segs. on the other chord when 2 chords intersect inside a ⊙.

Try This

7. ∠DGE and ∠FGC; ∠GDE and ∠GFC; ∠GED and ∠GCF; △DGE and △FGC are ~ △s by the AA ~ Post.

8. When 2 secants or 2 chords of a ⊙ intersect, 4 segs. will be formed, each with the pt. of intersection as 1 endpt. The product of the lengths of the segs. on 1 secant/chord will = the product of the lengths of the segs. on the other secant/chord.

   If a secant and a tangent of a ⊙ intersect at an ext. pt., 3 segs. will be formed, each with the ext. pt. as an endpt. The product of the lengths of the secant segments will = the square of the length of the tangent seg.

GEOMETRY LAB 12-6
Segment Relationships in Circles

Activity

10. They are congruent.

11. are congruent

Try This

4. 10

5. 3

Holt McDougal Geometry

ALGEBRA LAB 13-2
Exploring Probability Data

Try This

1. Answers will vary

2. Answers will vary according to how many colors; e.g. in this lab it is 1/6.

3. Sample Answer: Theoretical probability is the likelihood that the event will occur so it is not always accurate with the experimental probability which I based on carrying out the experiment a certain number of times. In fact, the experimental probability is likely to vary each time you conduct the same experiment.

4. As the number of events increases, the difference between the theoretical and experimental probability will decrease.

5. **a.** theoretical probability = 25%

   b. Sample answer: Close but not exact.

   c. About 25% of the time; as the number of events increases, the experimental probability will become closer to the theoretical probability.

TECHNOLOGY LAB 13-2
Explore Simulations

1. ≈ 16.9%

2. ≈ 2.6%

3. Possible answer: Use =INT(1000*RAND( )) 10 times. Consider numbers 0-284 successes.